It's another Quality Book from CGP

This book is for 7-8 year olds.

It contains lots of tricky questions designed to make you sweat — because that's the only way you'll get any better.

It's also got some daft bits in to try and make the whole experience at least vaguely entertaining for you.

What CGP is all about

Our sole aim here at CGP is to produce the highest quality books — carefully written, immaculately presented and dangerously close to being funny.

Then we work our socks off to get them out to you — at the cheapest possible prices.

Where to Find Things

These Homework Books closely match our classbooks A and B. They follow the National Numeracy Framework and each page is homework for one night. At the bottom of each homework book page there is a reference to the classbook pages covered.
To make it easier to find what you want, we've grouped them together here under the five main strands.

Numbers and the Number System

Calculations

Solving Problems

Measures, Shape and Space

Handling Data

Published by Coordination Group Publications Ltd.

Written and Illustrated by:
Chris Dennett Winner of the mushroom float competition at the age of 7.
Caroline Moore Made a vegetable caterpillar at the age of 6.
Kate Stevens Won a spelling bee at the age of 10.
James Paul Wallis Won the teddy bear lookalike contest at the age of 5.

With thanks to Claire Thompson for the Numeracy Strategy Research.

ISBN 1 841 146 061 3

Groovy website: www.cgpbooks.co.uk

Printed by Elanders Hindson, Newcastle upon Tyne.
Clipart sources: CorelDRAW and VECTOR.

Number Values

Q1 Write down the following in number form.

a) Eighty-two ....

b) Two hundred and fifty-seven ....

c) Four hundred and thirty-one ....

d) Nine hundred and ninety-nine ....

Let's get stuck in

Q2 Split these numbers into hundreds, tens and units.

	H	T	U		H	T	U
a) 126	100	20	6	d) 392			
b) 81				e) 411			
c) 982				f) 742			

Q3 Write the biggest and smallest numbers you can, using the three digits given. Give the biggest number first.

a) 2, 3, 1 ....

b) 4, 2, 9 ....

c) 8, 5, 7 ....

d) 6, 1, 5 ....

e) 9, 7, 8 ....

f) 2, 3, 5 ....

Q4 Draw arrows from the numbers to the position they should be on the number line (before Brian eats them all).

340, 333, 338, 342, 335, 348, 345.

330 350

Q5 Write down all the numbers between 34 and 42.

....

End of Page One

SEE CLASSBOOK A P.1-3

Double and Triple Addition

Q1 Find the answers to the following sums.

a) 2 + 4 = ... d) 12 + 8 = ... g) 14 + 12 = ...

b) 4 + 2 = ... e) 25 + 15 = ... h) 20 + 11 = ...

c) 10 + 8 = ... f) 18 + 8 = ... i) 17 + 21 = ...

Q2 Simple stuff over, it's time for the triple additions.

a) 2 + 4 + 4 = ... d) 19 + 5 + 5 = ...

b) 6 + 4 + 2 = ... e) 18 + 8 + 2 = ...

c) 10 + 6 + 4 = ... f) 23 + 9 + 11 = ...

Q3 Norman has twenty-four fish and he gets six more.

How many has he got now?
(Write out the sum, and answer it).

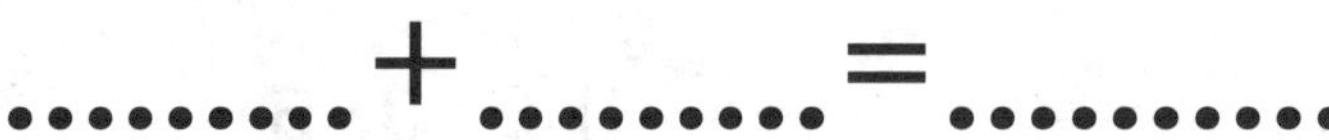

Q4 At seven o'clock, ten rabbits came for dinner. Fifteen more arrived at eight and twelve others came at nine o'clock.

How many rabbits came to dinner?
(Write out the sum, and answer it).

....

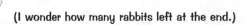

(I wonder how many rabbits left at the end.)

Double and Triple Subtraction

Q1 Take a breath and then do these subtractions.

a) 2 – 1 = ... d) 15 – 8 = ... g) 26 – 16 = ...

b) 4 – 2 = ... e) 19 – 11 = ... h) 45 – 10 = ...

c) 10 – 5 = ... f) 34 – 21 = ... i) 49 – 19 = ...

Q2 Triple subtractions — the fun just goes on and on.

a) 4 – 2 – 1 = ... d) 30 – 12 – 5 = ...

b) 6 – 4 – 1 = ... e) 37 – 15 – 4 = ...

c) 10 – 4 – 3 = ... f) 50 – 23 – 7 = ...

Q3 Garreth scored 51 points in an archery contest. The judges took away 13 points because Sinbad helped him. Then the judges took away 17 points because Garreth wasn't far enough away.

How many points did Garreth have in the end?

.... = ...

Q4 Now for some addition and subtraction on the same page.

a) 2 + 4 = ...6... so ...6... – 4 = ...2...

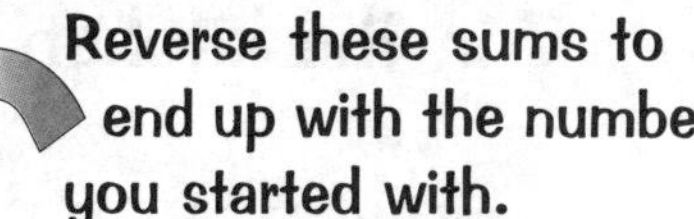

Reverse these sums to end up with the number you started with.

b) 5 + 14 = ... so .... – 14 = ...

c) 36 + 12 = ... so .... – 12 = ...

d) 92 + 13 = ... so .... – 13 = ...

SEE CLASSBOOK A P.4-6

Mental Strategies — Pairs That Make 10

Q1 Fill in the numbers needed to make the following add up to 10.

a) 4 + ... d) 8 + ... g) 1 + ...

b) 6 + ... e) 5 + ... h) 2 + ...

c) 9 + ... f) 3 + ... i) 7 + ...

Q2 Circle pairs of numbers that add up to ten and then link the pairs with a line. The first one has been done for you.

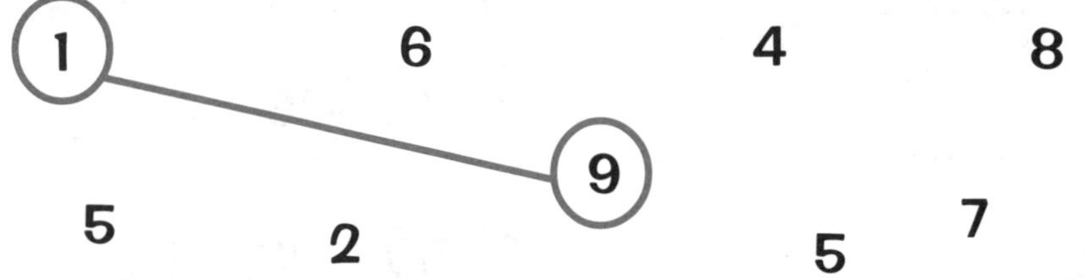

Q3 Find pairs that add up to 10 to help you answer these sums.

a) 2 + 8 + 1 + 9 = ? ......

....

Make up a new sum using the tens you have found.

b) 1 + 5 + 2 + 8 + 9 + 6 + 4 = ? ......

....

Q4 Kurt collects curly cats. He has 4 in the loft, 3 in the wardrobe, 6 in the garage, 8 in the treehouse, 7 in the kitchen, 2 in his bedroom, and 5 at school.

How many cats he has altogether? Write out the sum and then find pairs to help you answer it.

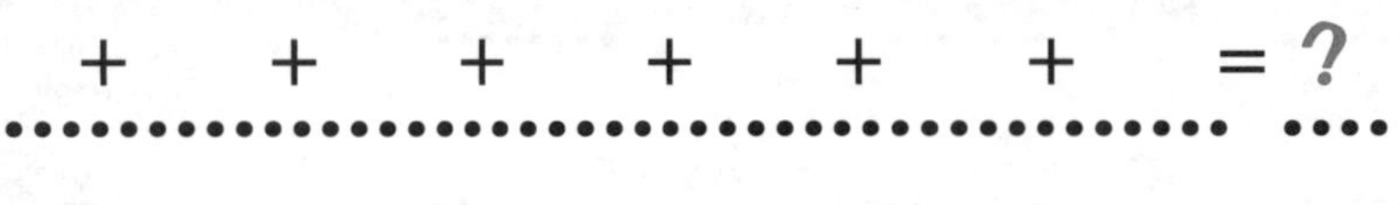

....

Write the sum out in full first, then write all the 10s out, then add them up.

Mental Strategies — 9 and 11

Q1 Do these sums by treating each 9 as a 10 and taking away the extra 1's at the end.

a) 7 + 9 = 7 + 10 − 1 = 16

b) 12 + 9 = ...

c) 25 + 9 = ...

d) 37 + 9 = ...

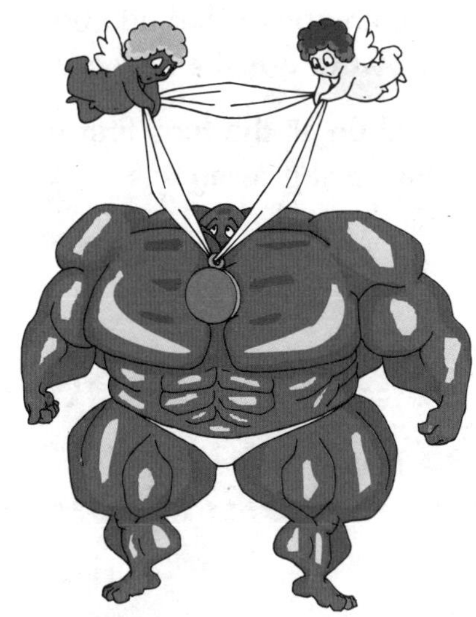

Q2 Do these sums by treating each 11 as a 10 and adding the extra 1's at the end.

a) 7 + 11 = 7 + 10 + 1 = 18

b) 24 + 11 = ...

c) 18 + 11 = ...

d) 46 + 11 = ...

Q3 Burly Bruce fought a moose to win him his 11th medal today. Yesterday he won 36 medals in the strongman poetry contests.

a) How many medals has he got in total? ....

b) How many would he have if he had only won 9 today? ....

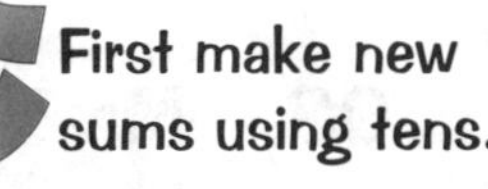

First make new sums using tens.

Q4 Correlli the robot shark is going for the world duration-skipping record. He has already skipped for 168 years and has to skip for 9 more years to equal the record.

What is the record at the moment? ....

SEE CLASSBOOK A P.7-9

Mental Strategies — Using 9 and 11

Q1 Circle pairs that add up to nine and box pairs that add up to eleven.

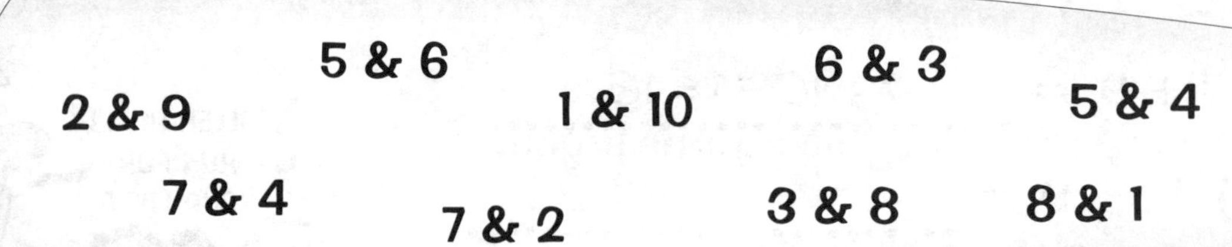

5 & 6 6 & 3

2 & 9 1 & 10 5 & 4

7 & 4 7 & 2 3 & 8 8 & 1

SPATULA-HEADED PETER

Q2 Find pairs that add up to 9. Then treat the 9s as 10s to make the sum easy. For each 9 you treat as a 10 take away the 1 at the end.

a) 17 + 2 + 7 + 5 + 4 = ?

Find any pairs that add up to 9 and write out the new sum.

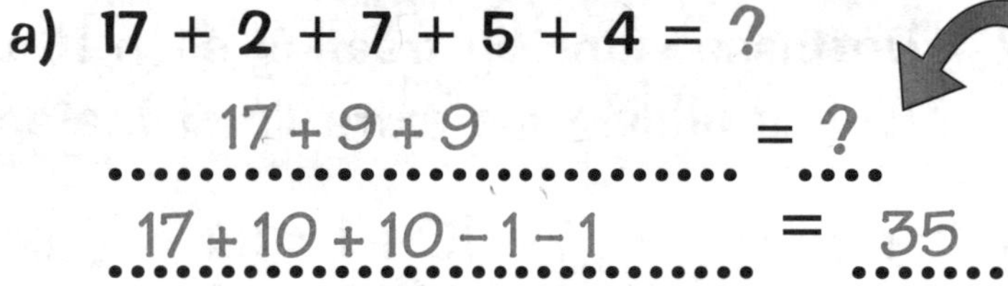

17 + 9 + 9 .... = ?....

17 + 10 + 10 − 1 − 1 .... = 35......

Add on all the tens first and leave the taking away till the end.

HAAAAAYYYYYAAAA!!

b) 16 + 4 + 5 + 3 + 6 = ?

.... = ?....

.... = ...

c) 4 + 5 + 6 + 3 + 1 + 8 = ?

.... = ?....

.... = ...

Q3 Mr. Bins has lots of pairs of glasses. He has 24 red pairs, 2 blue pairs, 7 yellow pairs, 5 black pairs and 4 white pairs.

How many pairs of glasses does he have?

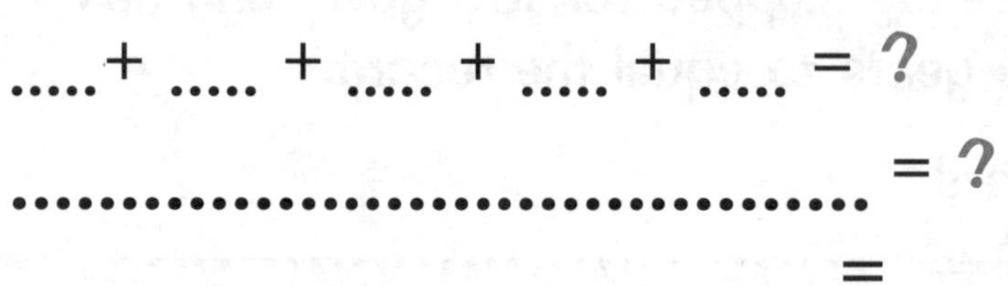

.....+ ..... + ... + ... + ... = ?

.... = ?

.... = ...

SEE CLASSBOOK A P.7-9

Money — Coin Value

Q1 Write in the values of the coins below.

Frongel the Moose has made the job harder by sticking them on their edges. There are a few clues to help you.

25 of these are worth one of these.

.... p

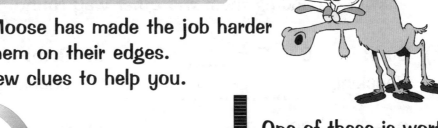

One of these is worth a hundred 1p's.

....

This is worth half as much as the one above.

....

This is the most expensive coin.

....

50p

A) ....

B) ....

Two A's and one B make 50p.

Q2 Which coin is missing from above? ....

If you had 20 of these you'd have £1.

Q3 Fill in the missing coins to make up the totals below.

50p + + + = 85p

+ + 10p + = 18p

+ + + 1p = £3.51

+ 5p + + = £1.08

SEE CLASSBOOK A P.10-11

Using Other Sums to Check Results

Q1 Add up these sums and then check the answer by adding them the other way round.

Example: 4 + 5 = 9
Checking: 5 + 4 = 9

a) Sum: 6 + 5 = ...
Checking: ....

b) Sum: 20 + 3 = ...
Checking: ....

c) Sum: 51 + 11 = ...
Checking: ....

d) Sum: 11 + 12 = ...
Checking: ....

e) Sum: 29 + 13 = ...
Checking: ....

f) Sum: 27 + 30 = ...
Checking: ....

Q2 Add up these sums and then check the answer using a subtraction sum.

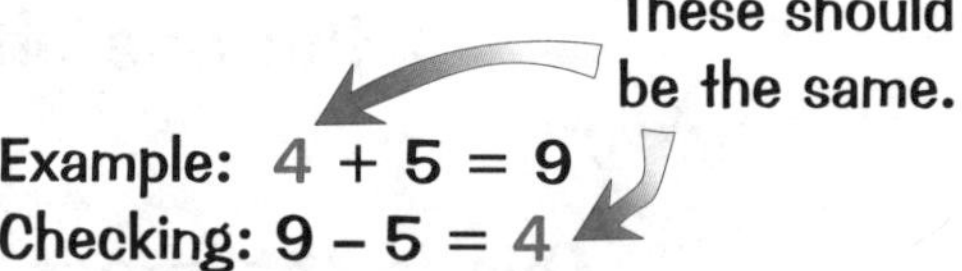

These should be the same.

Example: 4 + 5 = 9
Checking: 9 – 5 = 4

a) Sum: 7 + 3 = ...
Checking: ....

I'd do a few stretches before starting this lot.

b) Sum: 9 + 10 = ...
Checking: ....

c) Sum: 27 + 20 = ...
Checking: ....

d) Sum: 14 + 6 = ...
Checking: ....

e) Sum: 68 + 5 = ...
Checking: ....

Q3 Alan's got 52 points in the skateboarding competition. His last trick "inverted-stalefish-air" gets him 12 more points.

What is Alan's total score?

a) Write out a sum to find out Alan's score.

....

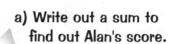

b) Use one of the checking methods to check the answer.

....

See Classbook A P.12-13

Measures — Taking Readings

Q1 Fill in the missing measurements.

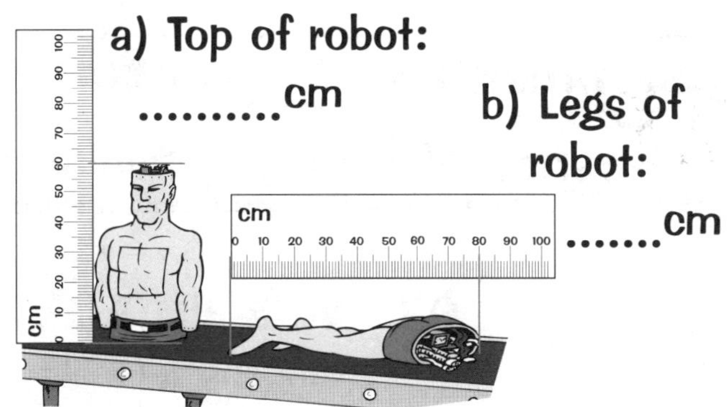

a) Top of robot:

..........cm

b) Legs of robot:

.......cm

c) Height of toy soldier:

..........cm

d) Height of soldier's shoulder:

..........cm

f) Amount of liquid:

....

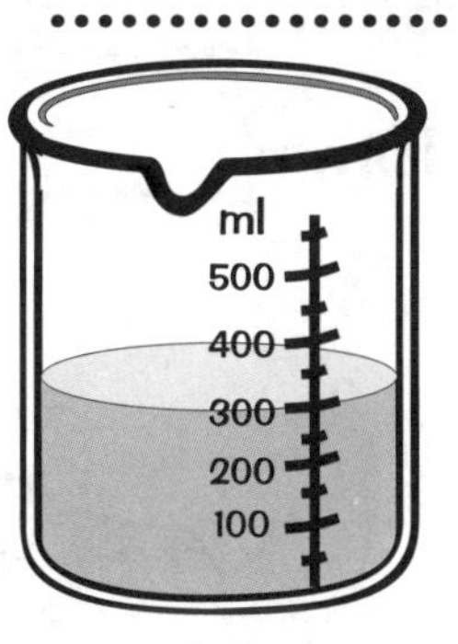

e) Amount of soup:

....

g) Weight of Penelope:

....

Q2 Professor Scaley needs 800ml of dino-juice to turn him into a full dinosaur. He's found four beakers, each with some juice in.

Write the amounts of each beaker in the sum and then answer it.

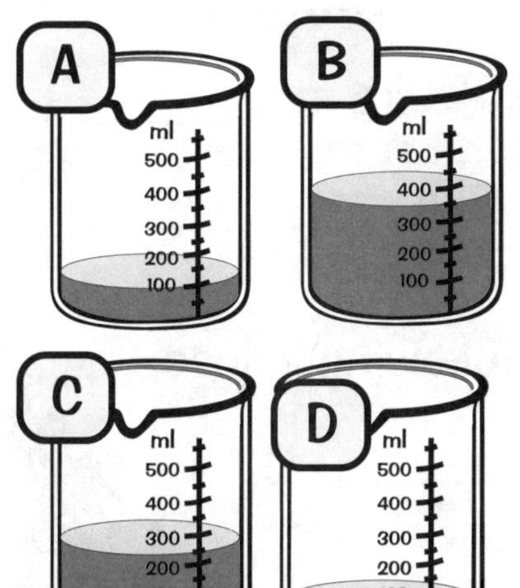

D

..........+..........+..........+..........=..........

Has he got enough juice? ....

Fill this beaker with the total amount of juice he has.

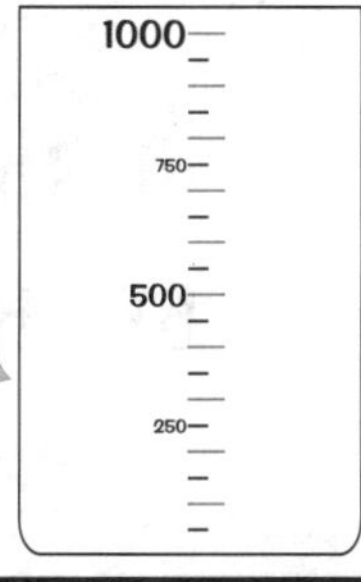

SEE CLASSBOOK A P.14-15

Measures — Changing Units

Q1 Fill in the numbers missing from Long John's back.

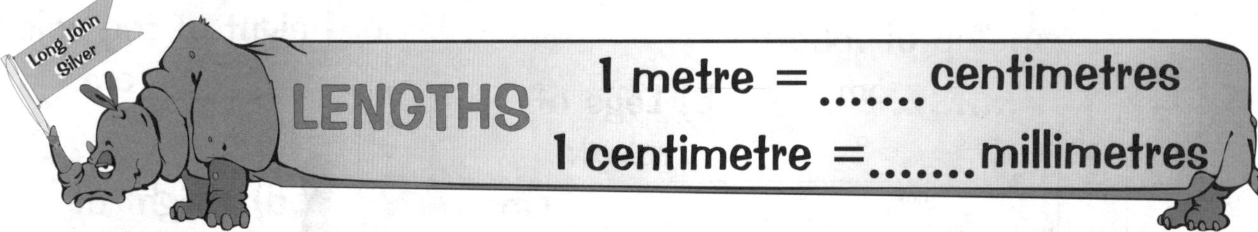

Q2 Write the following lengths in centimetres.

a) 3m ....
b) 6m ....
c) 20m ....
d) 100m ....
e) 10m ....
f) 32m ....
g) 50m ....
h) 10mm ....

Q3 Write the following lengths in millimetres.

a) 10cm ....
b) 100cm ....
c) 48cm ....
d) 1m ....

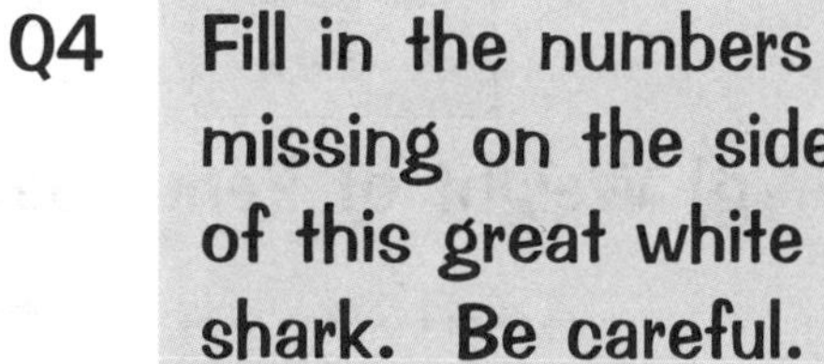

Q4 Fill in the numbers missing on the side of this great white shark. Be careful.

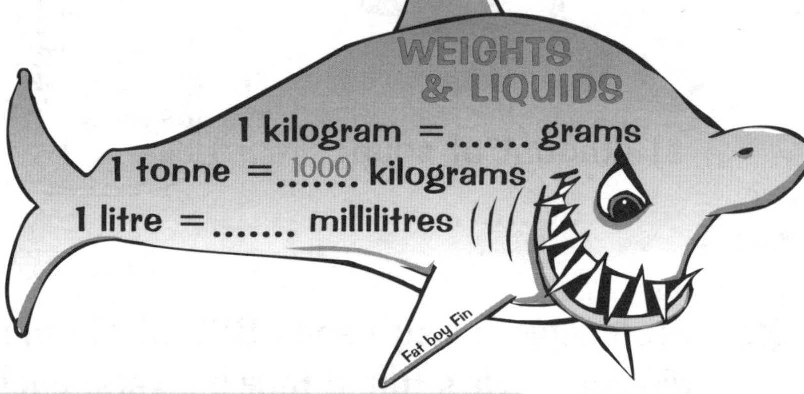

Q5 Convert the following into different measurements.

a) 1000ml = ...l
b) 2 tonnes = ...kg
c) 8000g = ...kg
d) 20l = ...ml
e) 2000kg = ...tonnes
f) 1.5kg = ...g

Q6 Give a sensible unit for measuring the following things.

a) The amount of water in a tea cup. ....
b) The weight of a house. ....
c) The length of a football pitch. ....

See Classbook A P.16-17

Shapes and Right Angles

Q1 Write down the number of sides and the names of each shape.

....

....

....

Q2 The drainpipe below has five circled angles.
Put a large tick over any that are right angles.

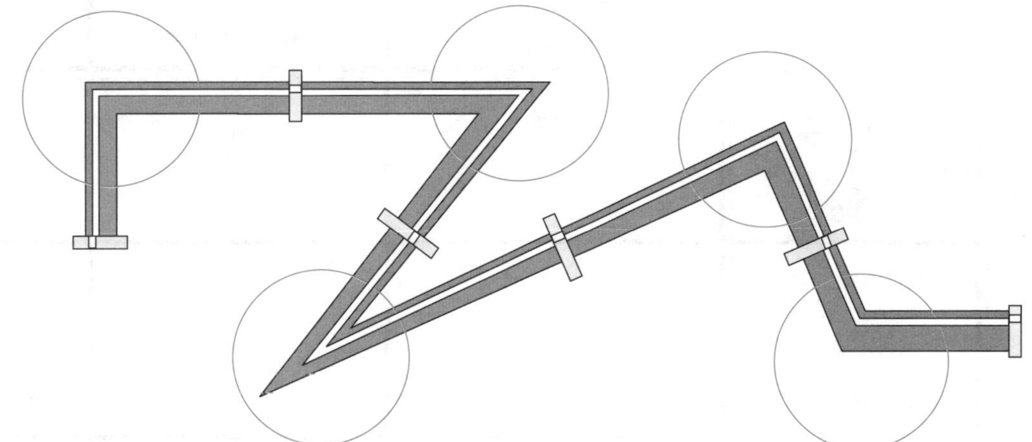

Q3 Name the solid shapes below.

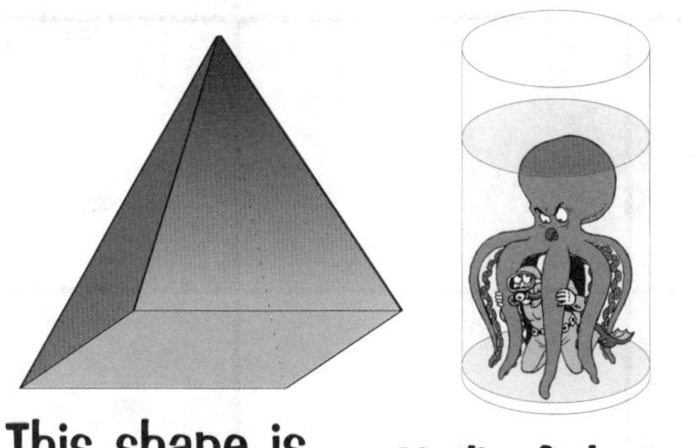

This shape is a ....

Neil's fish tank is a ....

The basketball is a ....

Trevor's Tepee is a ....

SEE CLASSBOOK A P.18-19

Shapes — Faces, Vertices and Edges

Q1 Fill in the gaps using these words.

Faces
Vertices *(corners)*
Edges

This is one of the cube's ....

This is one of the cube's ....

This is one of the cube's ....

Q2 Fill in all the gaps in this table.

	Number of faces	Number of vertices	Number of edges
	1	0	0
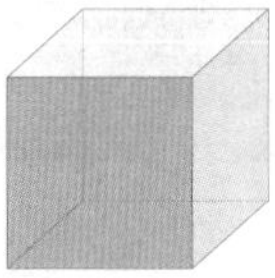			
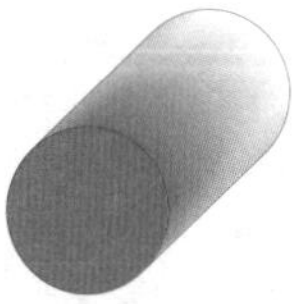			

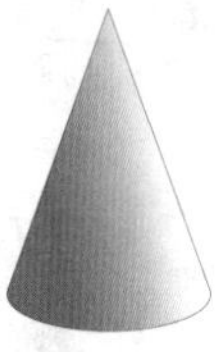			

SEE CLASSBOOK A P.20-21

Lines of Symmetry

Q1 Draw lines of symmetry on the following shapes.

The first one has been done for you.

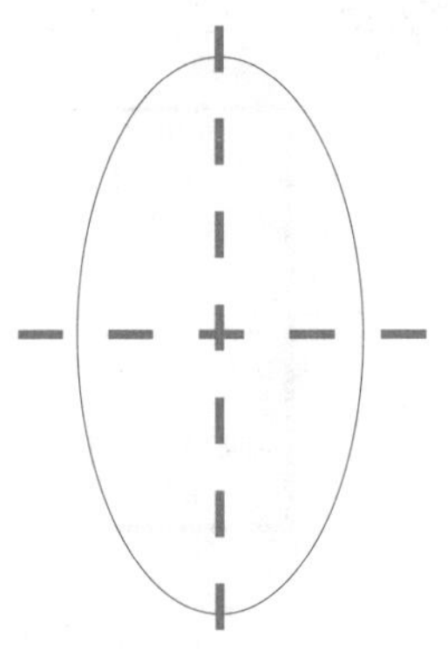

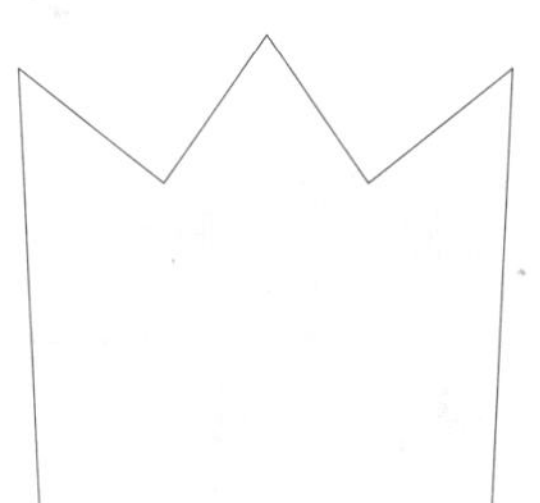

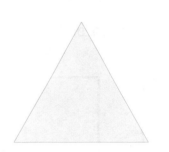

Q2 Here's some more of the same. These ones are a bit harder.

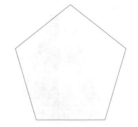

Q3 Use a mirror to help you draw on all the lines of symmetry for these three pictures.

① 

② 

③ 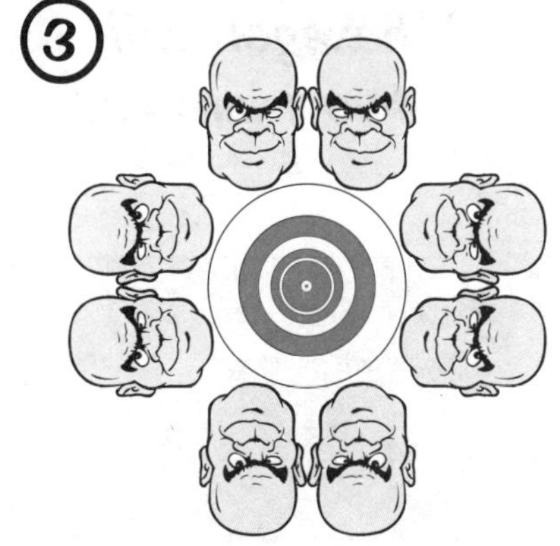

SEE CLASSBOOK A P.22-23

Investigating and Combining Shapes

Q1 Investigate the statement below and find the answer.

"You can draw two lines on a square to make four triangles."

Use these squares to try out different ideas

Put the correct answer in this square.

Q2 Name the shapes below that are made out of two triangles and one rectangle.

Choose from these shape names:
triangle, square, rectangle, pentagon, hexagon, octagon.

....

....

....

Q3 Use the space to prove that the following statement is WRONG.

"You can't make a hexagon with these two triangles."

Counting With Groups and Patterns

Q1 Late at night when all is dark, all the shadows hold sporting events. It costs each shadow £4 to enter the competition.

Count up the total amount of money as each competitor pays.

Q2 Filbert was beginning to wonder whether it really had been a dream.

Find out how many spiders there are using the grouping method.

First you have to find as many groups of five as you can, and then add on the remainder.

.... × 5 + ...

TOTAL = ...

Q3 **For each of the following, write down the next even number.**

a) 6 .... c) 121 .... e) 24 ....

b) 17 .... d) 59 .... f) 330 ....

Q4 **For each of the following, write down the previous odd number.**

a) 3 .... c) 15 .... e) 10 ....

b) 100 .... d) 61 .... f) 299 ....

SEE CLASSBOOK A P.26-29

Reasoning with numbers — Puzzles

Q1 Find four different odd numbers that add up to 16.

You must use all the boxes and you can't use the same number twice.

Q2 Find six different numbers under ten that add up to 30.

Think about pairs that add up to ten.

Q3 Fill in the blank circles by following the rules below.

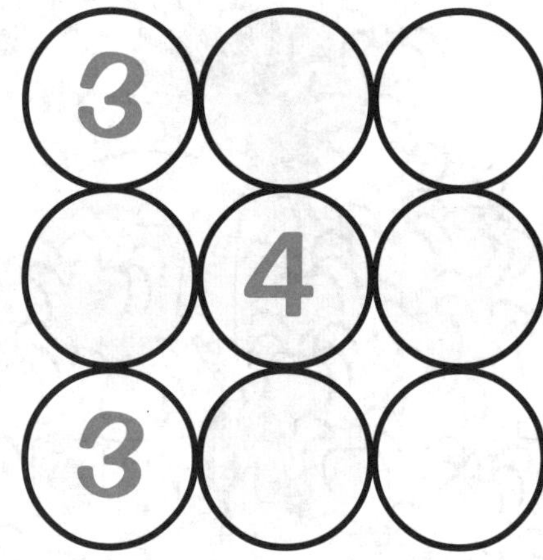

Rules:

1) Each row must add up to ten.
2) Each column must add up to ten.
3) You can't use zero.

(There are three possible solutions.)

Q4 Icarus is trying to do sums while plummeting at terminal velocity towards the city of Swansea.

Very fast.

Write the hidden numbers on the clouds before he lands.

2 + ☁ = 10 7 + ☁ = 19

72 − ☁ = 72 99 − ☁ = 4

51 − ☁ = 10 138 + ☁ = 165

Understanding '×' & '÷'

Q1 Work through this batch of easy multiplication sums.

a) $4 \times 2 =$ .... e) $5 \times 3 =$ ....

b) $4 \times 4 =$ .... f) $3 \times 8 =$ ....

c) $10 \times 5 =$ .... g) $7 \times 5 =$ ....

d) $6 \times 8 =$ .... h) $8 \times 6 =$ ....

Jam-jar Jim

Remember if you get stuck you can use the adding method. 7×5 can be done by adding seven, five times.
$7 + 7 + 7 + 7 + 7$

Q2 Now some lovely division sums to keep your brain pumping.

For these you could use the subtraction method. $10 \div 2$ can be done by taking 2 away from 10 until you get 0. The number of 2's you subtract is the answer.
$10 - 2 - 2 - 2 - 2 - 2$

a) $10 \div 2 =$ .... e) $8 \div 4 =$ ....

b) $15 \div 5 =$ .... f) $16 \div 4 =$ ....

c) $12 \div 3 =$ .... g) $25 \div 5 =$ ....

d) $50 \div 5 =$ .... h) $50 \div 10 =$ ....

Q3 Cleaver girl chops up sugar into cubes to give to her 4 horses. She's made 44 sugar cubes today.

How many cubes will each horse get if she shares them out evenly? Write out the whole sum.

....

Q4 Sam has sold 7 packets of 9 doggy nuggets to tourists.

How many fake dog poo nuggets has Sam sold altogether? Write out the whole sum.

....

SEE CLASSBOOK A P.32-36

Understanding '×' & '÷' as Opposites

Q1 Plough through these easy multiplications involving 10 and 100.

Sinking Stan

Remember you just add '0' when you multiply by 10 and '00' when you multiply by 100.

a) $3 \times 10 =$ ....

b) $8 \times 10 =$ ....

c) $72 \times 10 =$ ....

d) $2 \times 100 =$ ....

e) $23 \times 100 =$ ....

f) $10 \times 100 =$ ....

Q2 These questions use multiplication and division sums.

Slap-headed Frank

Remember to look at the multiplication sums to help you answer the division sums.

a) $6 \times 2 = 12$, so $12 \div 6 =$ ...2... and $12 \div 2 =$ ...6...

b) $11 \times 4 = 44$, so $44 \div 11 =$ .... and $44 \div 4 =$ ....

c) $13 \times 29 = 377$, so $377 \div 13 =$ .... and $377 \div 29 =$ ....

d) $99 \times 97 = 9603$, so $9603 \div 99 =$ .... and $9603 \div 97 =$ ....

Q3 Jean-Paul eats seven flowers every day for four days.

How many flowers does he eat altogther?

Do the multiplication sum. .... × .... = ...

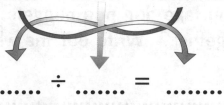

Now check it using division.
(The numbers linked by arrows should be the same if the sum is correct.) .... ÷ .... = ...

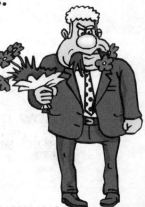

2, 5 and 10 Times Tables

Q1 Fill in the missing numbers from these times tables sums.

a) 2 × 2 = ... b) 2 × 5 = ...

c) 10 × 7 = ... d) 2 × 9 = ...

e) 4 × 5 = ... f) 10 × .... = 50

g) ...... × 2 = 16 h) 5 × .... = 30

i) 2 × 12 = ... j) 5 × 11 = ...

Q2 Complete the times tables below.

1 × 2 = 5 × 2 = 9 × 2 =

2 × 2 = 6 × 2 = 10 × 2 =

3 × 2 = 7 × 2 = 11 × 2 =

4 × 2 = 8 × 2 = 12 × 2 =

1 × 5 = 2 × 5 = 3 × 5 =

4 × 5 = 5 × 5 = 6 × 5 =

7 × 5 = 8 × 5 = 9 × 5 =

10 × 5 = 11 × 5 = 12 × 5 =

1 × 10 = 5 × 10 = 9 × 10 =

2 × 10 = 6 × 10 = 10 × 10 =

3 × 10 = 7 × 10 = 11 × 10 =

4 × 10 = 8 × 10 = 12 × 10 =

 SEE CLASSBOOK A P.37

Multiplication & Division — Real Life(ish)

Q1 Each Meerkat burrow contains 5 Meerkats.

What is the total number of Meerkats in the following burrows.

a) 2 burrows ...... × ...... = ...

b) 4 burrows ...... × ...... = ...

c) 5 burrows ...... × ...... = ...

d) 7 burrows ...... × ...... = ...

Q2 A rhino's heart beats 10 beats per minute.

How many times will a rhino's heart beat in the following times?

a) 3 minutes ...... × ...... = ...

b) 5 minutes ...... × ...... = ...

c) 10 minutes ...... × ...... = ...

Q3 A crack team of 4 moles have been sent to the moon. They have been given a load of food that they must divide equally between them.

Work out how much each mole will get.

a) 8 chocolate bars. ...... ÷ ...... = ...each

b) 44 beans. ...... ÷ ...... = ...each

c) 100 worms. ...... ÷ ...... = ...each

d) 24 slugs. ...... ÷ ...... = ...each

Q4 Faggle Batwingface has got 75 jokes to write in only 15 days. How many must he write each day to split the work evenly?

....

Fractions — Shapes, Numbers & Robots

Q1 Fluke Piesquawker has been chopping up stuff with his light sabre.

Shade in the fraction written next to each shape.

a) One half.

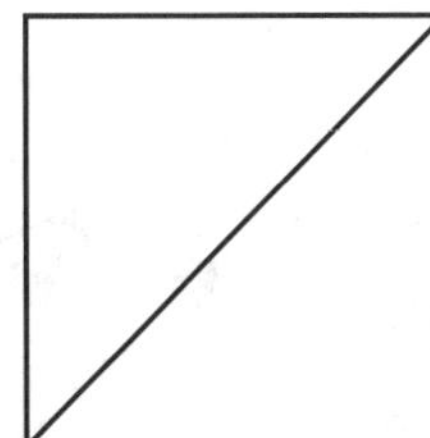

b) One quarter.

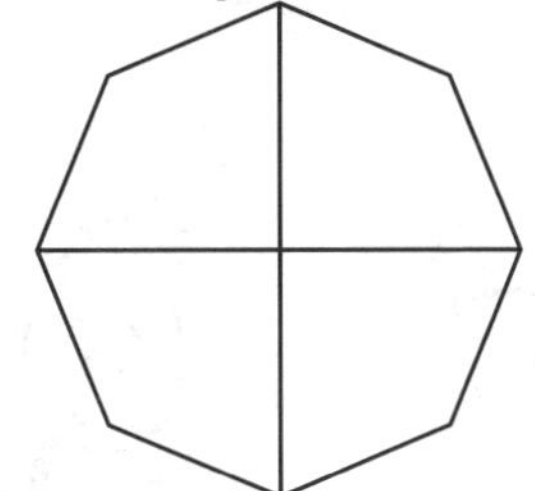

c) One third.

d) One half.

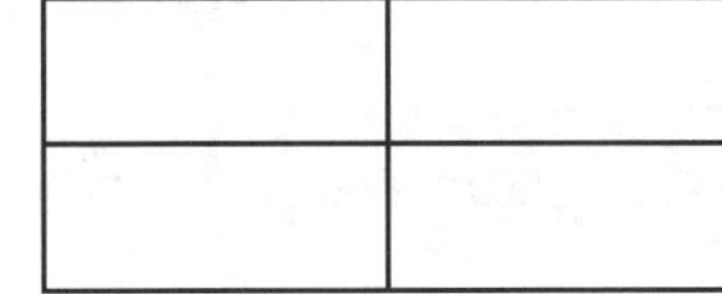

e) Two fifths.

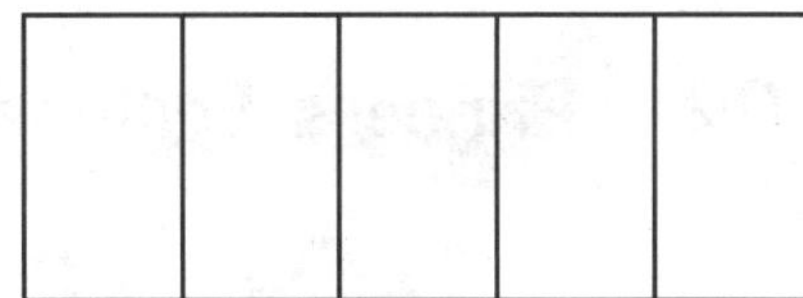

Q2 Boneyone Kenobi has set Fluke some sums as part of his training.

Change the questions into sums before answering them.

a) What is one half of 24 stars? .... ÷ .... = ... stars.

b) What is one third of 30 robots? .... ÷ .... = ... robots.

c) What is one fifth of 25 battleships? .... ÷ .... = ... battleships.

d) What is one tenth of 80 droids? .... ÷ .... = ... droids.

Q3 **Put a ring around seven tenths of Bath Wader's robot bodyguards.**

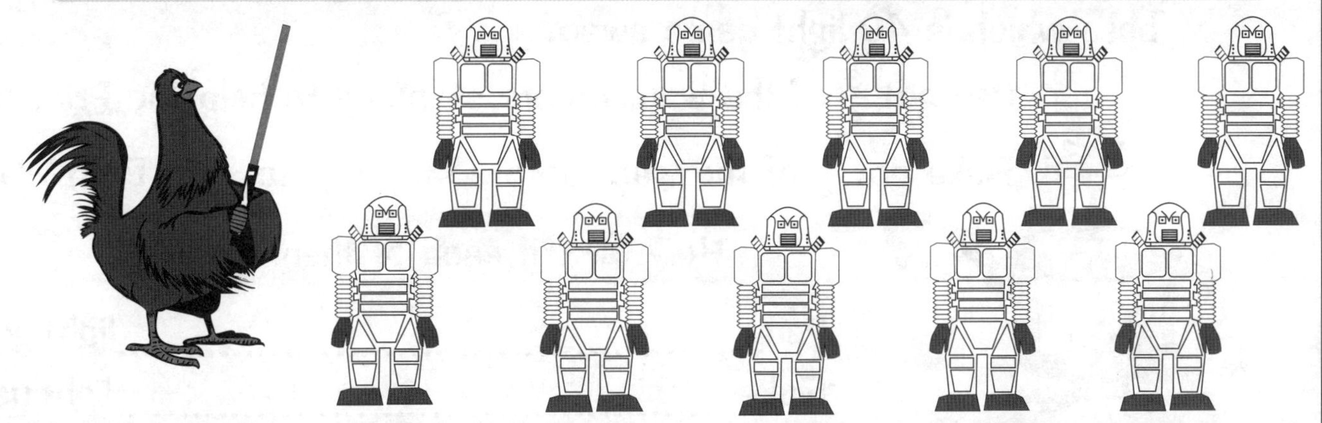

See Classbook A P.41-43

Fractions — Number Lines

Q1 Attach each fraction droid to the right part of the number line.

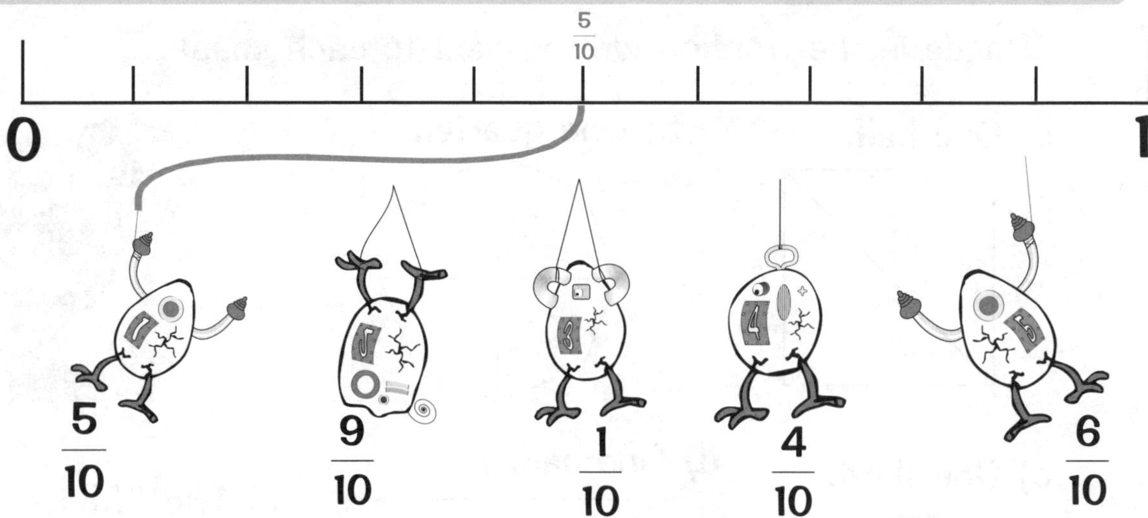

Q2 Princess Egglayer needs your help to find the following fractions.

$\frac{3}{4}$, $\frac{1}{4}$, $\frac{1}{2}$ – put these on the number line below.

0 ———————————————— 1

Q3 Work out the fractions of the following numbers.

a) $\frac{1}{3}$ of 66 ....

b) $\frac{1}{4}$ of 24 ....

c) $\frac{3}{4}$ of 100 ....

Remember to divide by the bottom number and then multiply by the top number.

Q4 Fluke Piesquawker and Pan Holo are racing to get to the enemy base which is 40 light years away.

Pan got $\frac{3}{4}$ of the way, before stopping to help the Princess.

Fluke got $\frac{1}{4}$ of the way, before stopping to fight Bath Wader.

How far did each of them travel?

Pan...light years.

Fluke...light years.

'+' & '–' Using Hundreds, Tens & Units

Q1 Write these three digit numbers out as hundreds, tens and units.

564 is ...... hundred, ... tens and ...... units.

759 is ...... hundred, ... tens and ...... units.

899 is ...... hundred, ... tens and ...... units.

783 is ...... hundred, ... tens and ...... units.

Easy
stuff

Q2 Work out these sums using one sum for each of the digits.

8 – 7 =
5 – 3 =
856 – 733 = 123
6 – 3 =

a) 555 – 234 = ...

b) 968 – 612 = ...

c) 835 – 125 = ...

d) 423 + 272 = ...

e) 371 + 221 = ...

f) 845 + 154 = ...

g) 352 + 614 = ...

Q3 Sam Ham has already won 437 medals at pig rodeos. This year he has won 252 more.

How many medals does he have now?

.... + ... = ... medals.

Q4 Add up these sums by adding up the multiples of 5 and 10 first.

a) 11 + 16 = 10 + 15 + 1 + 1 = ...

b) 16 + 17 = 15 + 15 + 1 + 2 = ...

c) 12 + 21 = ... + ... + 2 + 1 = ...

d) 17 + 26 = 15 + 25 + ... + ... = ...

e) 12 + 26 = ... + ... + ... + ... = ...

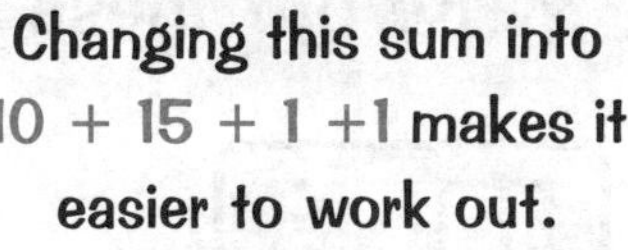
Changing this sum into
10 + 15 + 1 +1 makes it
easier to work out.

They're all
staring at me.

SEE CLASSBOOK A P.46-47

Measures — Clocks

Q1 Write out the times underneath each clock.

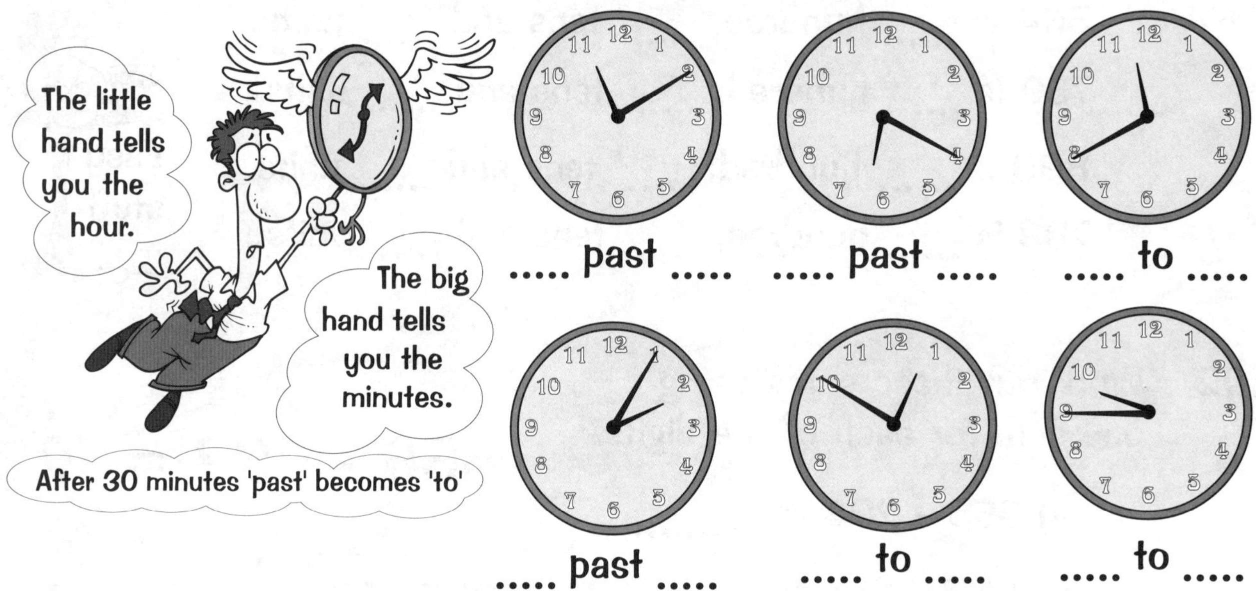

The little hand tells you the hour.
The big hand tells you the minutes.
After 30 minutes 'past' becomes 'to'
..... past .....
..... past .....
..... to .....
..... past .....
..... to .....
..... to .....

Q2 Write down these clock times in digital form. They're all morning.

Q3 Write out these digital times in words. Again they're all morning.

07:15 ....

03:45 ....

10:55 ....

04:35 ....

02:05 ....

Remember to use "PAST" for less than thirty minutes and "TO" when it's over thirty minutes.

Handling Data — Tallies and Tables

Q1 Here is a table showing the result of an ultimate computer fighting competition.

	Karate Kate	Wrestling Rhonda	Wendy
Fights Won	111	16	0
Fights Lost	0	52	114
Fights Drawn	13	4	0
Special Move	Shoulder chop	Bum drop	Face Slap

a) How many fights has Rhonda lost? ....

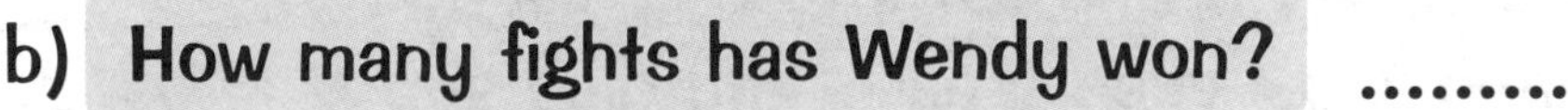

b) How many fights has Wendy won? ....

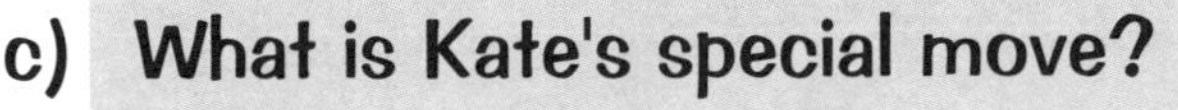

c) What is Kate's special move? ....

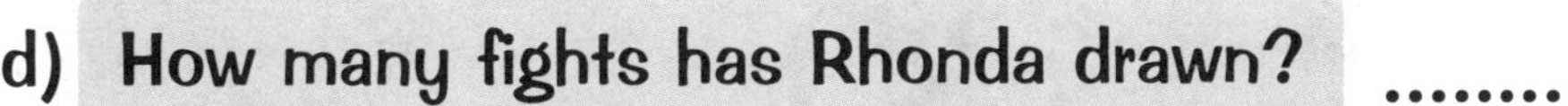

d) How many fights has Rhonda drawn? ....

Q2 Mr Tibor has got a shop full of exotic fish.

Count all his things using a tally chart and then put in the totals.

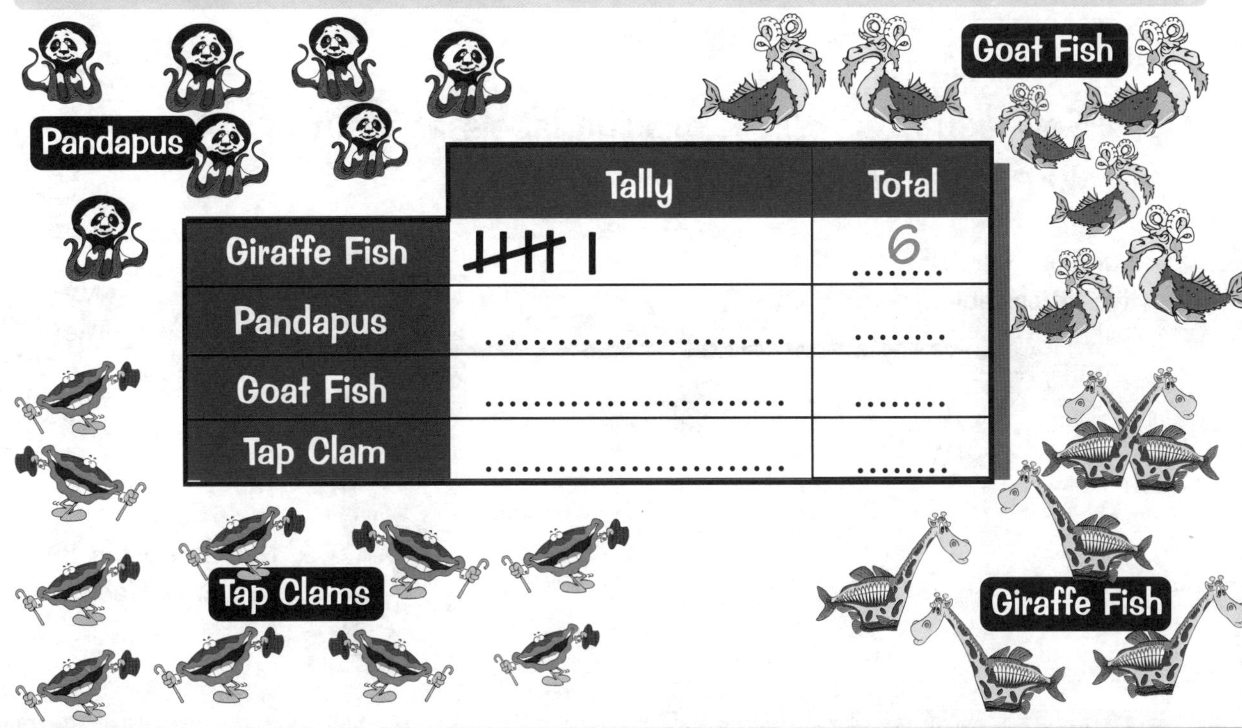

	Tally	Total
Giraffe Fish	~~IIII~~ I	6
Pandapus	....	....
Goat Fish	....	....
Tap Clam	....	....

SEE CLASSBOOK A P.50-51

Handling Data — Grouping Things

Q1 On the diagram opposite, label one group "dairy products" and one group "not dairy products".

tigers
peas
yoghurt
butter
lions
rain
milk
cheese
rocks
clouds

....
....

Use the diagram to write down 2 things from each group.

Dairy products:

....

....

Not dairy products:

....

....

Q2 Now things get a little trickier.

Put the numbers 6, 14, 3 and 25 into the diagram. There is one number for each area in the diagram.

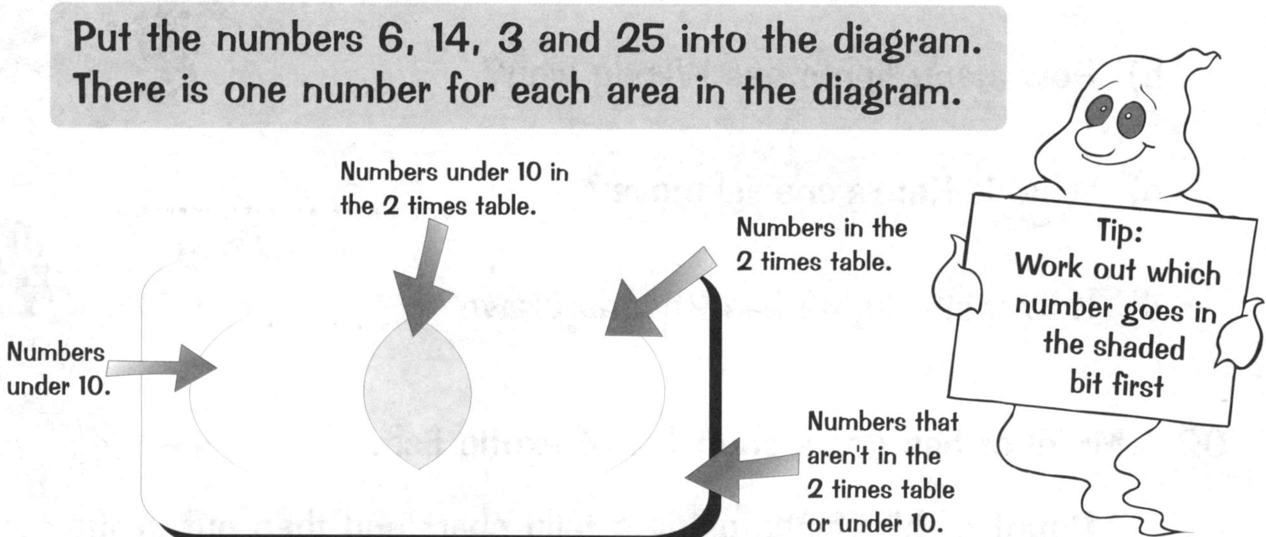

Q3 Now you've got fill in missing labels and put in your own numbers.

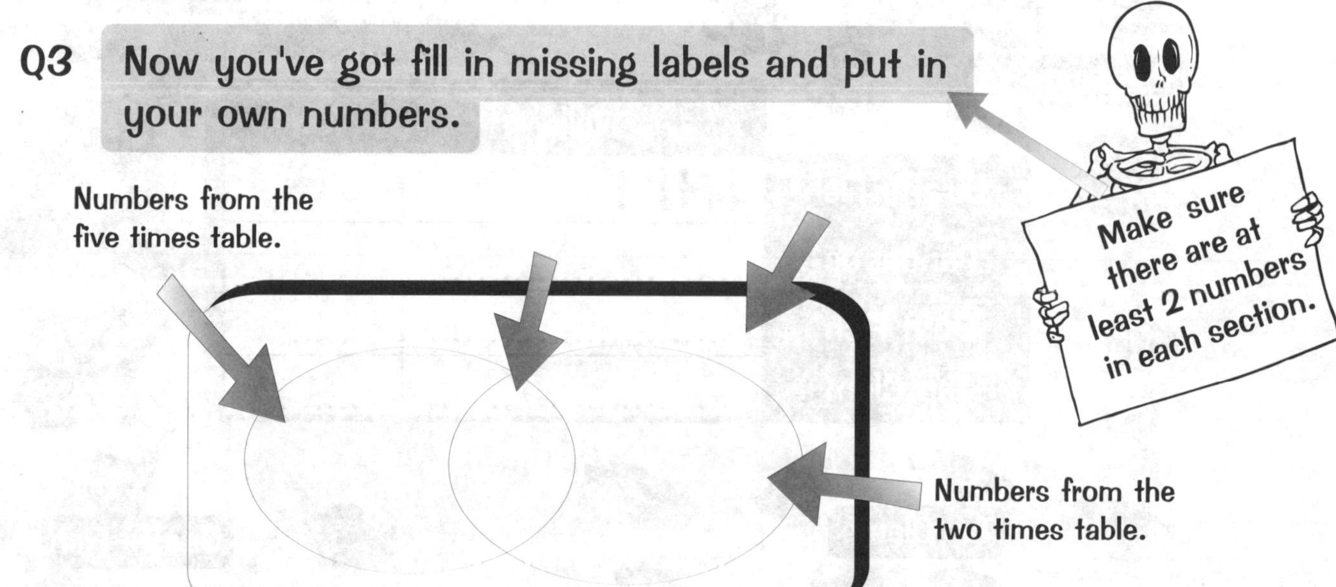

Numbers from the five times table.
Make sure there are at least 2 numbers in each section.
Numbers from the two times table.

Estimating

Q1 The Millennium Budgie school bus picks up pupils from all over the galaxy. It usually picks up about 7 pupils from each stop. For every pupil on the bus the noise level rises about 2 decibels.

Fill in the table, estimating the number of pupils and the noise level on the bus.

Number of stops	Est. number of pupils on the bus.	Est. noise level in decibels
1	7	14
3		
2		
5		
4		

Q2 Ned Land is fishing with a huge jam jar. Each time he hauls it out of the water he catches 2 giant cod and 6 ship wrecks.

Looking at the picture estimate the weight of the giant cod.

Ned: 100kg

Cod: ....

How many giant cod will he have after 5 goes with the jar?

Total number of cod ....

Use your estimated weight of one cod.

Total weight of the cod = ... × .... = ...

How many times will he have to haul up the jar before he has 30 ship wrecks?

....

See Classbook A P.54

Rounding and Reading Scales

Q1 Round the numbers below to the nearest ten.

11 .... 18 .... 46 ....

5 .... 55 .... 84 ....

114 .... 235 .... 991 ....

Remember if a number is exactly in the middle, then choose the bigger number.

Q2 Round these numbers to the nearest hundred.

101 .... 116 .... 280 ....

927 .... 351 .... 349 ....

641 .... 87 .... 961 ....

Q3 Round these measurements to the nearest metre.

99cm .... 262cm .... 415cm ....

851cm .... 64cm .... 912cm ....

956cm .... 742cm .... 749cm ....

Remember to put the right units in after every answer.

Q4 Write in the readings to the nearest whole number.

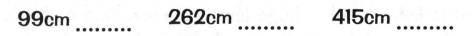

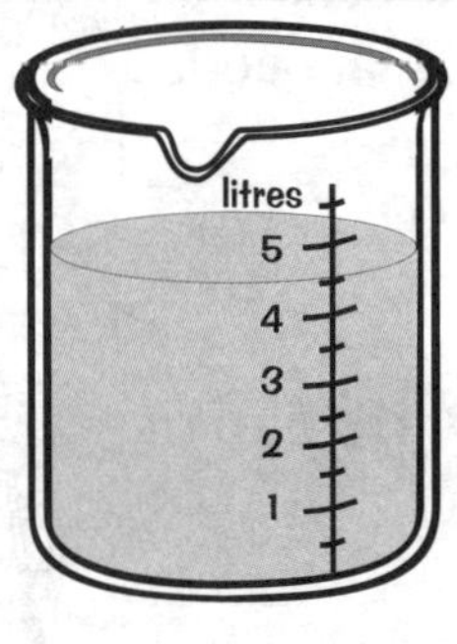

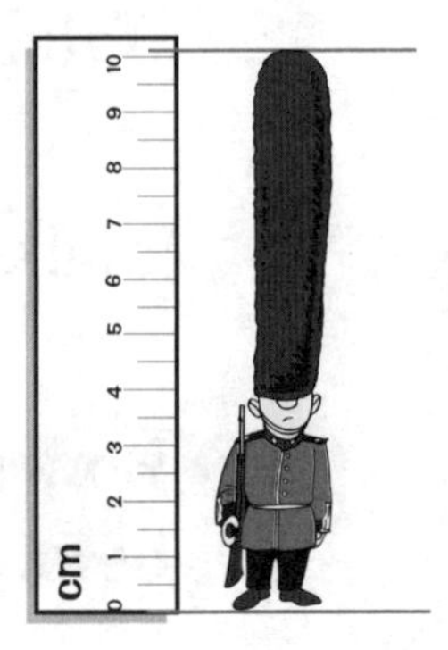

....

SEE CLASSBOOK A P.55-56

Doing Sums in Your Head

Q1 Do these addition sums in your head by counting on in ones.

a) 567 + 7 = ... b) 888 + 13 = ...

c) 293 + 9 = ... d) 328 + 6 = ...

e) 927 + 18 = ... f) 684 + 14 = ...

g) 456 + 14 = ... h) 87 + 13 = ... i) 156 + 8 = ...

Q2 Now do these subtraction sums in your head.

a) 247 – 238 = ... b) 789 – 777= ....

c) 999 – 981= .... d) 451 – 447 = ...

e) 323 – 315 = ... f) 686 – 677 = ...

g) 496 – 481 = ... h) 747 – 734 = ...

Q3 Use the numbers in the hedgehogs to complete the sentences.

If you add 6 to .... and then add .... you get 21.

If you add 21 to .... and then take away .... you get 17.

If you start with the 27 and add .... and .... you get 47.

If you add 3 to ...... and ...... and then take away 2 you get 40.

 SEE CLASSBOOK A P.57-59

Money, Money, Money

Q1 Change the amounts below from pounds to pence.

a) £3.00 = ...p b) £1.50 = ...p c) £2.25 = ...p

d) £8.57 = ...p e) £4.05 = ...p f) £4.91 = ...p

g) £10.20 = ...p h) £7 = ...p i) £12.09 = ...p

Q2 Change this lot from pence to pounds.

a) 100p = £.......... b) 522p = £.......... c) 405p = £..........

d) 498p = £.......... e) 312p = £.......... f) 909p = £..........

g) 101p = £.......... h) 111p = £.......... i) 1111p = £..........

Q3 Major Backpain bought himself some bargain hiking gear. He got a penknife for 155p, a walking stick for £3.45 and a huge rucksack for £6.41.

How much did he spend altogether?

Write out the sum. ➡ .... + ... + ...

Change all the numbers into pounds and answer it. ➡ .... + ... + ... = ...

Q4 Tim spent his pocket money on some tennis gear. He bought two projectile insoles for £2.50 each and a ball for 89p.

How much did he spend altogether?

....

....

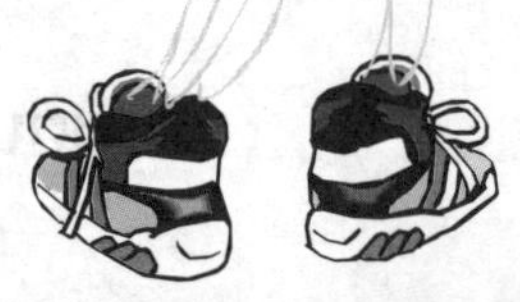

Mental Calculations with Money

Q1 Work out the cost of these meals in your head.

a) Zombie Chicken and small Peppered Eyes = £.......·........

b) Large Biteback Soup and Chef's Surprise = £.......·........

Biteback Soup	80p(small), 90p(large)
Zombie Chicken	£2.50
Chef's Surprise	£3.50
Peppered Eyes	£1(small), £1.20(large)

c) Chef's Surprise and Zombie Chicken = £.......·........

d) Large Peppered Eyes and small Biteback Soup = £.......·........

e) Small Peppered Eyes, Zombie Chicken and large Soup = £......·.......

Q2 Choose meals from the menu above, that cost the following prices.

a) £1.80 ....

b) £4.70 ....

c) £3.70 ....

d) £2.10 ....

Q3 Complete the table by saying if the change given is right or wrong.

Price charged	Amount paid	Change received	Right or Wrong?
£2.30	£5	£2.70	....
£7.30	£10	£1.70	....
£6.85	£20	£12.15	....
£4.45	£10	£5.55	....
£6.62	£20	£13.38	....

SEE CLASSBOOK A P.62-63

Grids and Dragonflies

Q1 Write the grid positions in each white square in (eg B1).

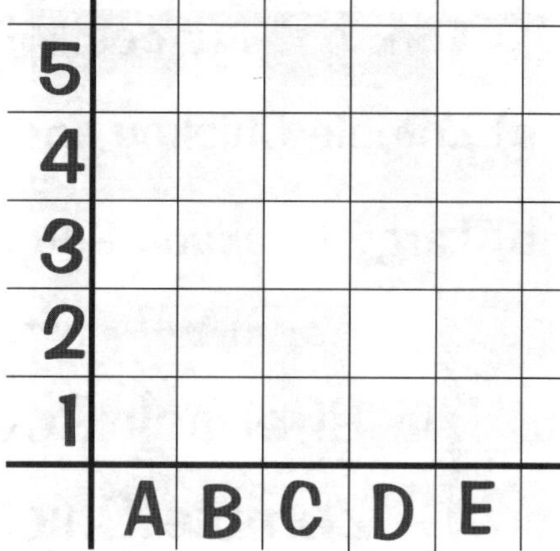

Q2 Shade in squares: C2, C3, C4, C5, C6, D2, D6, E2, E4, E6, F3, F4.

7
6
5
4
3
2
1
A B C D E F G H I J

What letter have you made?

....

Q3 Give the grid positions of each character.

① Hurdle Harry ....

② Billy Bike ....

③ Stella Sledge ....

④ Skiing Ian ....

⑤ Ryan Wrestle ....

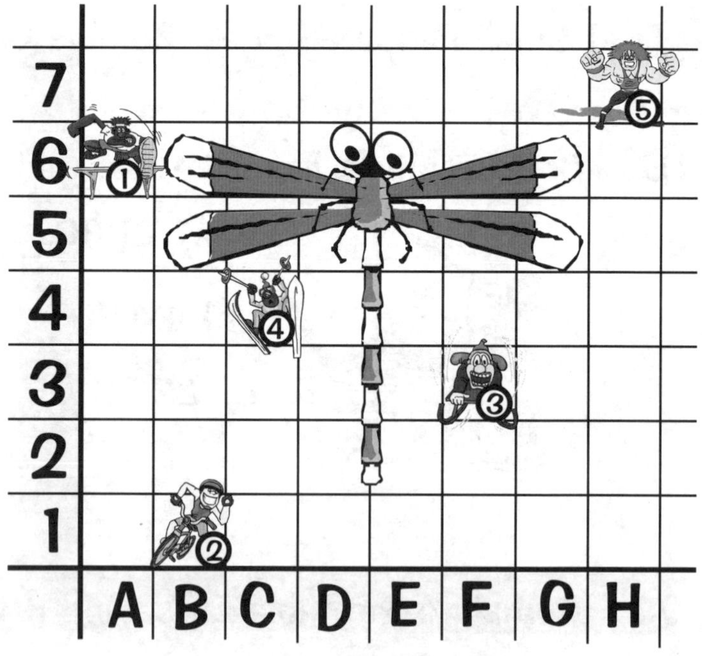

Q4 Describe the route that Billy should take to get to Stella.

Right ...... squares, and .... squares.

Q5 Describe the route that Ian should take to get to Ryan.

....

Directions and Snowmen

Q1 Help Pete find his pineapple by completing the directions.

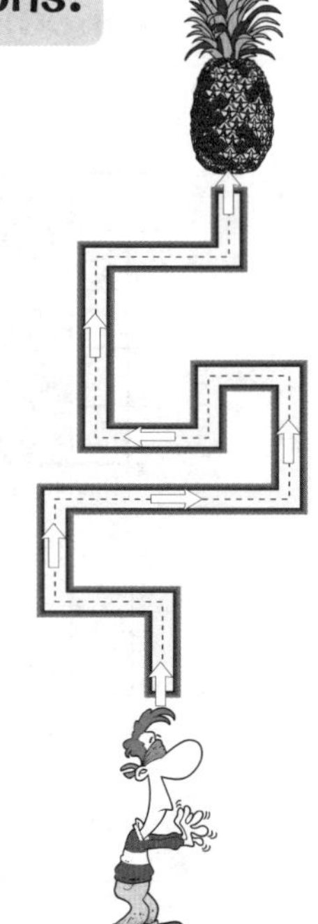

Go forward,
turn a right angle anticlockwise then go forward,
turn a right angle clockwise then go forward,
turn a right angle .... then go forward,
turn a right angle .... then go forward,
turn a right angle .... then go forward,
turn a right angle .... then go forward,
turn a right angle .... then go forward,
turn a right angle .... then go forward,
turn a right angle .... then go forward,
turn a right angle .... then go forward,

Q2 Fill in the missing letters from the compass directions.

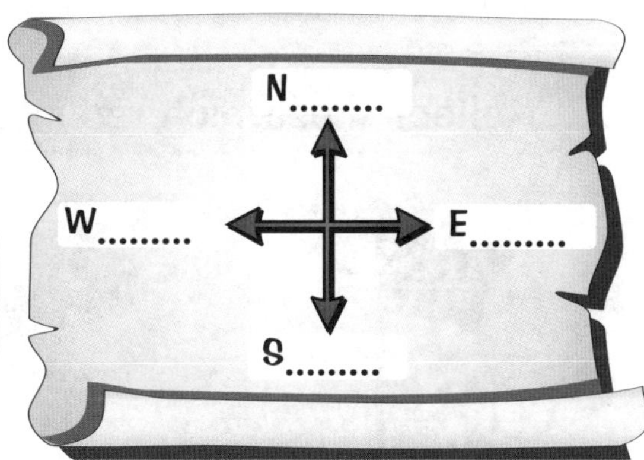

What direction is one right angle turn, clockwise from north?

....

Q3 Describe how each creature could get to the scared hunter.

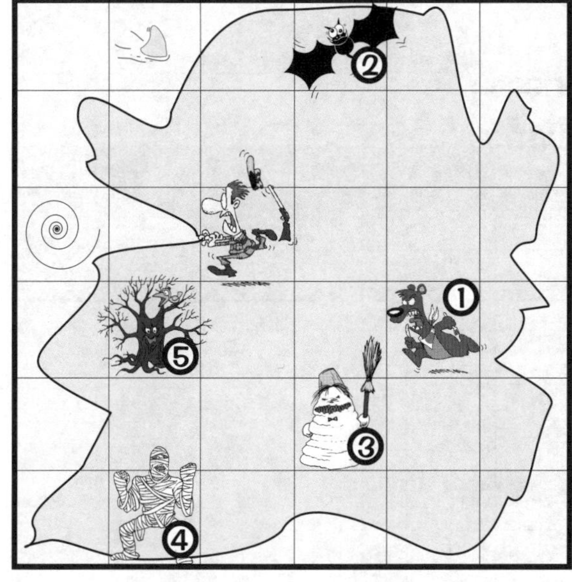

N

① Hungry Bear
2 squares west and 1 square north.

② Mad bat
....

③ Psycho snowman
....

④ Mr. Mummy
....

⑤ Magic tree
....

SEE CLASSBOOK A P.66-67

Reflecting Shapes and Pictures

Q1 Reflect each of these shapes in the mirror line.

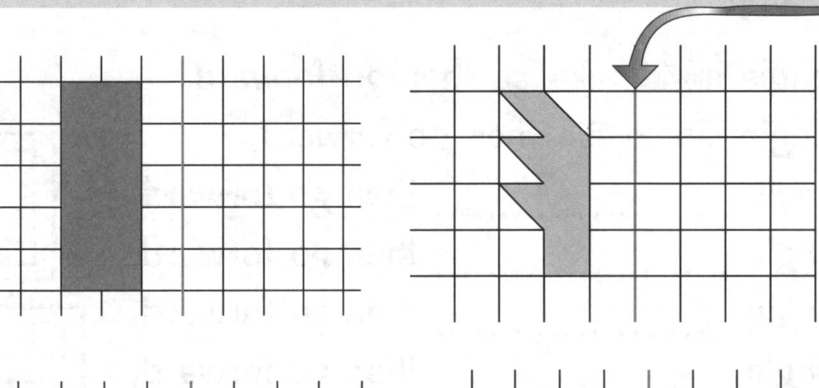

Mirror line
If you have a mirror, put it here to help you.

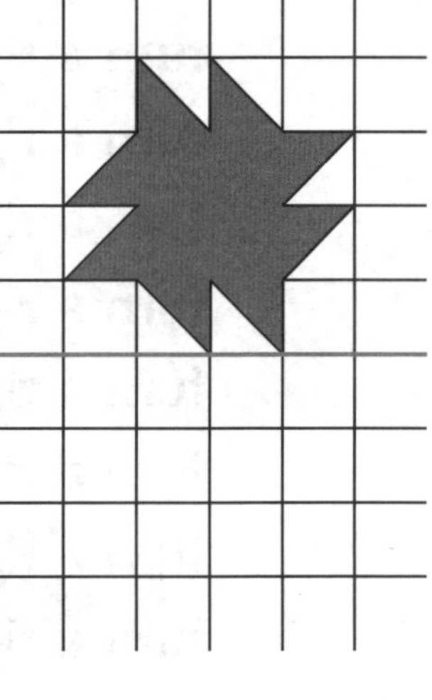

Q2 Reflect these pictures in the mirror line.

Artist/ maths Tips
Use the grid to help you to see where bits start and finish.

Q3 Complete these patterns to make them symmetrical in the mirror lines shown.

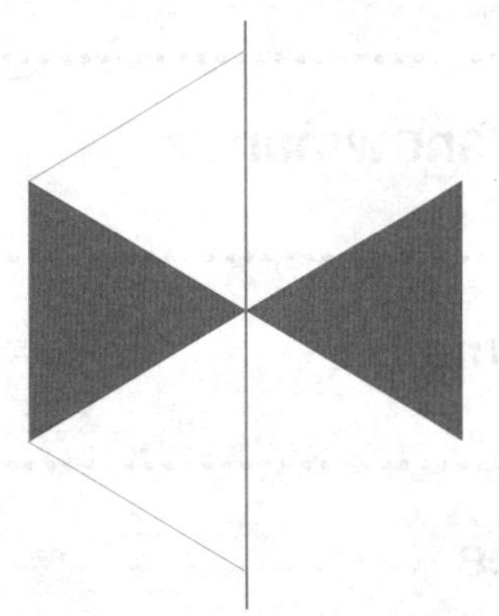

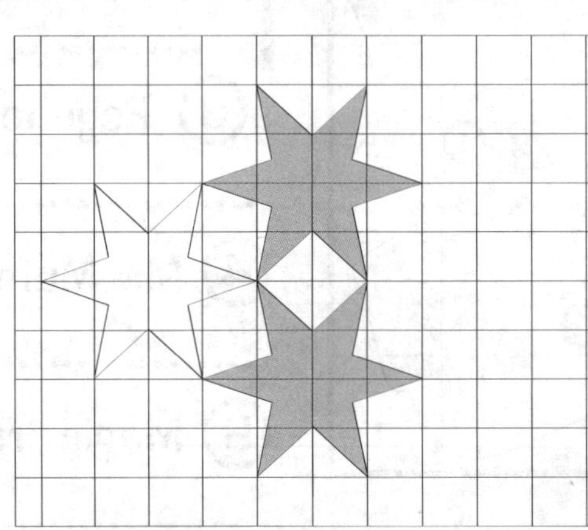

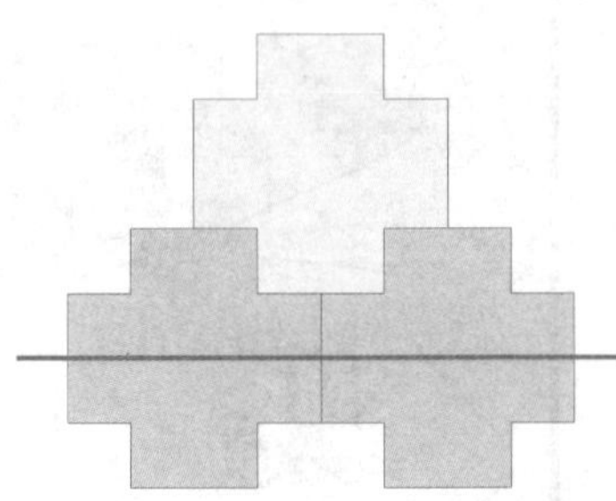

Measures and Time

Q1 Estimate the measurements of the following.

The length of your little finger: ....cm.

Your height in centimetres: ....cm.

Your height in little fingers: ....little fingers.

The weight of this book: ....

The number of words on this page: ....

The number of words in this book: ....

Q2 Suggest suitable units of time to use when estimating these.

Time taken to travel from London to Paris on the train: ....

Time taken to tie a shoelace ....

Time taken for your hair to grow 2m ....

Q3 What equipment would you use to measure each of the following?

a) Room temperature ....

b) Length of your hand ....

c) Length of a table ....

d) Your weight ....

e) 50ml of water ....

f) Height of a horse ....

Q4 Use the information given to make an estimate.

Last year 20 people got scorched by electric worms. Estimate how many people will be worm-scorched in 6 years. ....people.

Roger took 11 seconds to run 100 metres. Estimate how far he can run in 33 seconds.

....metres.

SEE CLASSBOOK A P.70-73

100 Squares, Number Lines & Sum Rules

Q1 These pictures are from a hundred square.
Fill in the blank squares using the rules below.

Move down one — add ten. Move up one — take away ten.
Move across one — add one. Move back one — take away one.

a)

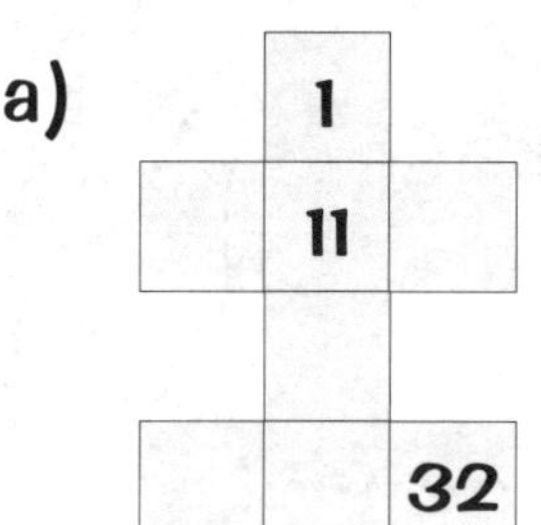

b)

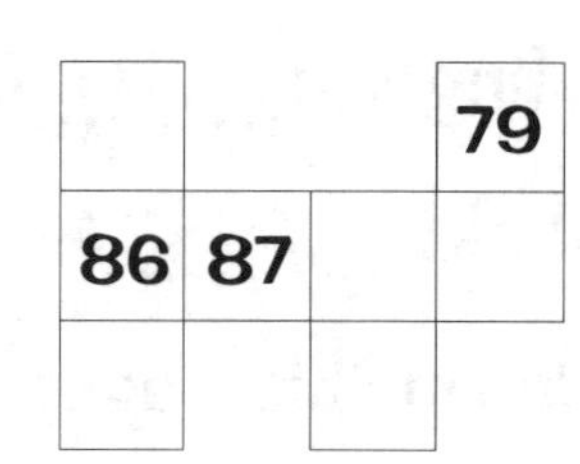

c)

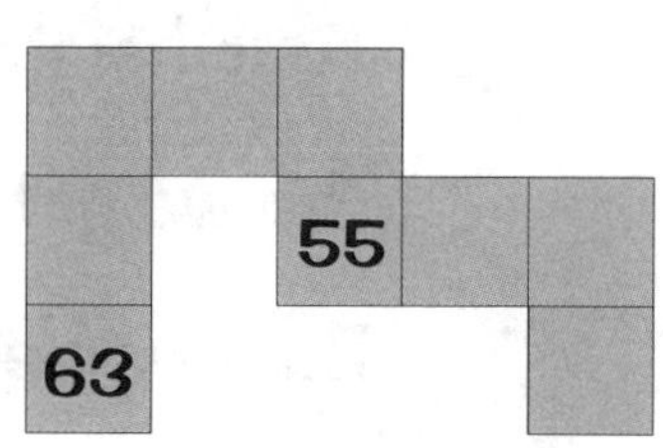

Q2 Answer the questions about number lines below.

a) Put the numbers 2.5, 5, and 7.5 on the number line opposite.

0 10

b) Put the numbers 10, 50 and 75 on this line.

0 100

Q3 Do the simple sums below.

2 + 8 =......... 3 + 7 =......... 6 - 2 =.........

13 - 3 =......... 20 + 4 =......... 19 + 3 =.........

14 - 8 =......... 27 - 9 =......... 20 + 40 =.........

Looking at your answers above, fill in odd or even in the spaces.

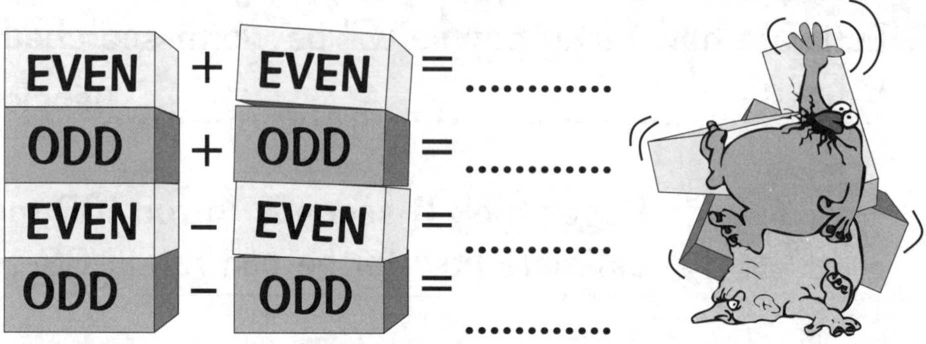

Number Sequences

Q1 Complete the next three numbers for the following sequences.

Hee hee!
My new brain
will do all my
homework.
BUILD-A-BRAIN

a) 2, 4, 6, 8, ..., ..., ...

b) 10, 15, 20, 25, ..., ..., ...

c) 7, 10, 13, 16, ..., ..., ...

d) 222, 322, 422, 522, ..., ..., ...

Q2 Complete the descriptions for the following number sequences.

a) 1, 3, 5, 7, 9. "Add ...... each time".

b) 3, 53, 103, 153, 203. "Add ...... each time".

c) 9, 17, 25, 33, 41. "Add ...... each time".

d) 13, 24, 35, 46, 57. "Add ...... each time".

Q3 Crystal has wired up her new build-a-brain to do her homework.

It has come up with two rules about numbers, test whether the rules are true by doing some simple sums in the space below.

RULE 1: If you add an even number to an odd number you always get an odd number.

RULE 2: If you add three to a number you always get an odd number.

....

....

....

....

....

....

....

....

Rule 1: true / false

Rule 2: true / false

SEE CLASSBOOK B P.4-5

Doubles and Nearly Doubles

Q1 Neville put 6 newts in his garden pond. He read that the number of newts would double after a week.

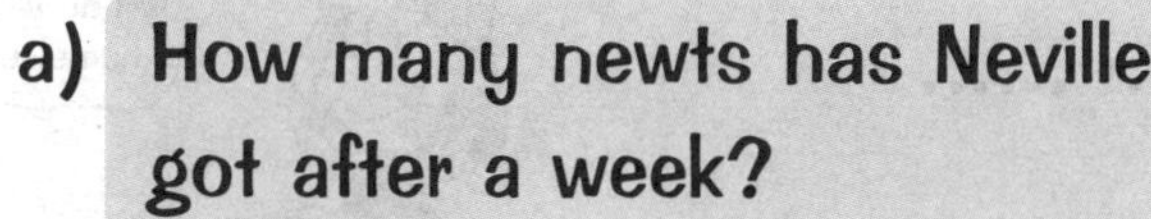

a) How many newts has Neville got after a week?

....

b) Another week passes. How many newts does he have now? ....

Hint: double your answer from a).

c) How many newts would you have to double to get 28 newts? ....

Q2 Add up these numbers that are nearly doubles.

If it wasn't for your wacky haircut we'd be doubles.

a) 15 + 16 = Double 15 + 1

= 30 + 1

= 31

Just write out the second two bits on the rest of these sums.

b) 30 + 31 = ...

= ....

c) 25 + 26 = ...

= ....

d) 17 + 18 = ...

= ....

e) 51 + 50 = ...

= ....

f) 50 + 49 = ...

= ....

For this one double 50 and then take away 1.

g) 65 + 66 = ...

= ....

h) 29 + 30 = ...

= ....

Multiples

Q1 Say what number these are all multiples of.

a) 2, 4, 6, 8, 10 .... b) 6, 9, 12, 15, 18 ....

Q2 What is...

a) the next multiple of 5 after 25? ....

b) the next multiple of 7 after 35? ....

I guess that's 'multi-bulls'!

c) the multiple of 4 before 20? ....

d) the multiple of 25 before 125? ....

Q3 Which of these numbers are a multiple of 5?

5, 32, 19, 20, 47

....

How can you tell? ....

....

Q4 Is 73 a multiple of 2? How can you tell?

....

Q5 You can only play Super Seated Skittles if the number of players is a multiple of 4.

Can this group play? ☐ Yes ☐ No

(There are 24 people.)

Q6 Carl's computer has spat out 67 letters. It will stop when the number of letters it has spat is equal to the next multiple of 50.

How many will that be? ....

The amount of letters stuck in his hair, is a multiple of 6.
If there are less than 20, what's the most there could be? ....

SEE CLASSBOOK B P.8-11

Money and Making Decisions

Q1 If I save £2 each day, for 13 days, how much will I have saved? ....

How much would I save...

a) in 16 days? ....

b) in 3 weeks? ....

c) in 4 weeks? ....

Q2 Heinster saves £4 each week so that he can buy a new water ski, which costs £40. How many weeks will it take?

....

How long would it take if each week he saved...

a) £5? .... b) £8? .... b) £2? ....

How much does he need to save each week to buy it in 4 weeks? ....

Q3 Fill in the circles with the correct operation (+, –, ÷ or ×).

a) 15 ◯ 6 = 9 b) 4 ◯ 3 = 12 c) 3 ◯ 11 = 14

d) 20 ◯ 5 = 4 e) 14 ◯ 7 = 7 f) 6 ◯ 2 = 3

Q4 Turn these bits of writing into sums and answer them.

Bunty the dog gets 24 magic peas for dinner.

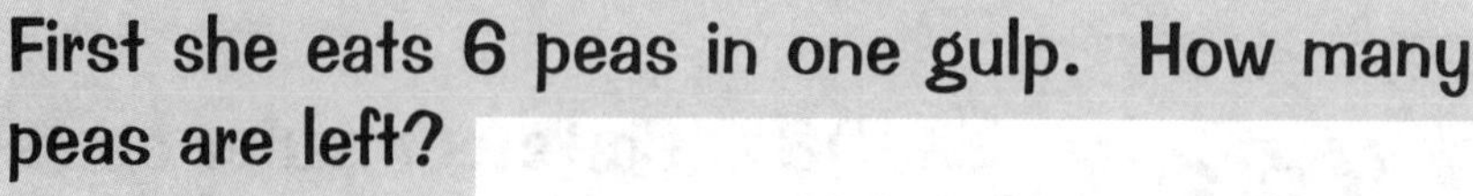

First she eats 6 peas in one gulp. How many peas are left?

....

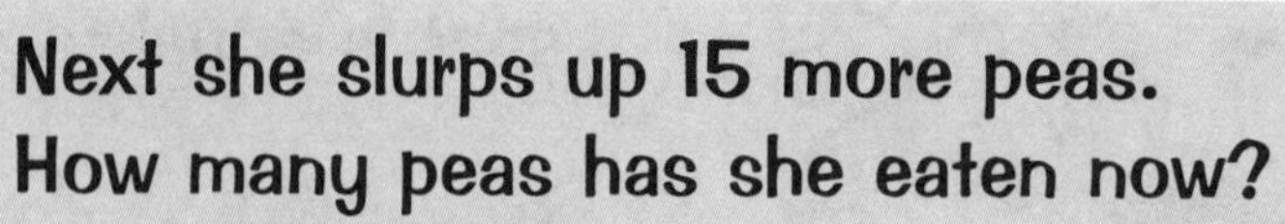

Next she slurps up 15 more peas. How many peas has she eaten now?

....

If the 24 magic peas were shared between 3 dogs how many would they get each? ....

Fractions — Number Lines and Objects

Q1 Make a mark $\frac{2}{5}$ of the way along this number line.

Is it usually so windy
at this time of year?

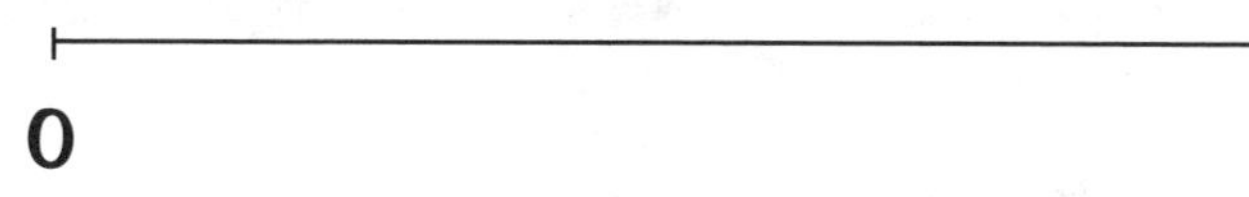

0
1

Q2 Mark and label these fractions on the number line below.

a) $3\frac{1}{2}$

b) $5\frac{1}{4}$

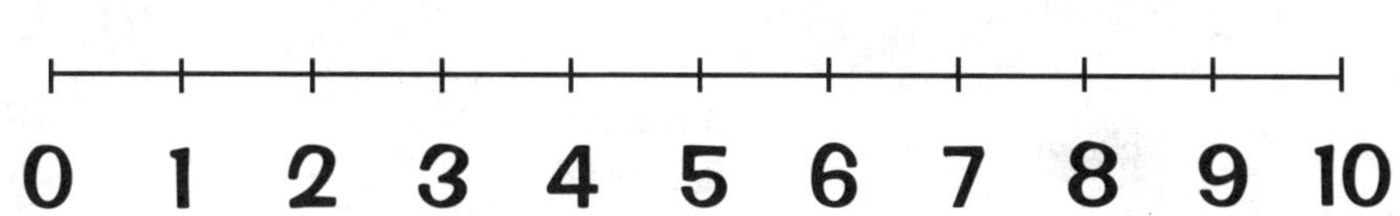

Q3 Are these statements true or false?

a) $\frac{1}{3}$ of the pizza has been eaten.

TRUE / FALSE

b) $\frac{3}{4}$ of the pizza has not been eaten.

TRUE / FALSE

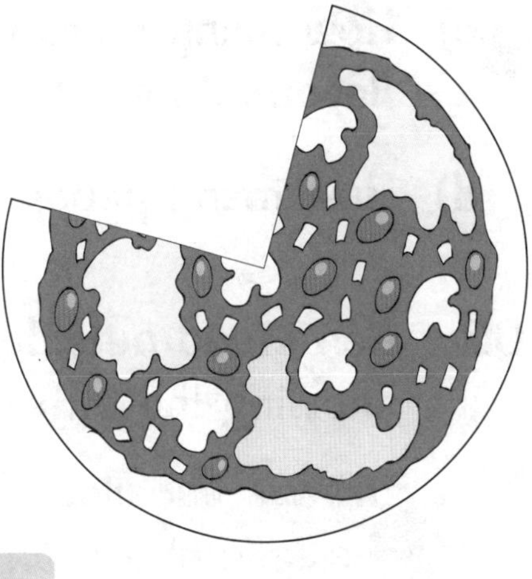

Q4 Estimate and fill in the missing fractions.

a) What fraction of the milk in the bottle has Pouncer drunk?

About ....

b) What fraction of the candles have been lit? ....

c) What fraction of the candles have not been lit? ....

SEE CLASSBOOK B P.16-19

Handling Data — Bar Charts

Q1 Look at the bar chart below, and answer the questions.

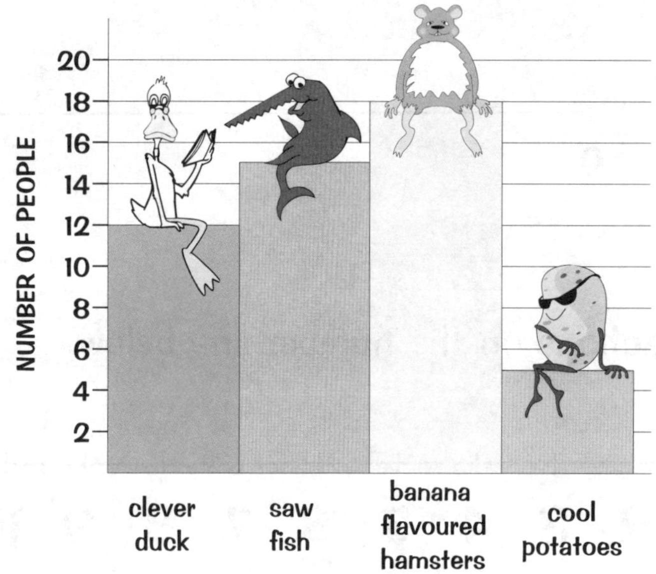

This bar chart shows the favourite foods of a number of people.

a) How many people like clever duck?

....

b) Do more people eat saw fish or cool potatoes?

....

c) How many more people eat banana flavoured hamsters than cool potatoes? ....

d) How many people took part in this survey? ....

Q2 Ben stood outside his house for 15 minutes and made a tally chart showing the different types of cars that drove past.

Draw a bar chart below using the information from the tally chart, and then answer the questions.

Car Type	Hatchback	Saloon	Van	Spaceship
Tally	𝍸 ||	𝍸	𝍸	|||

a) How many hatchbacks passed Ben's house?

....

b) What was the total number of saloons and spaceships to pass Ben's house?

....

Handling Data — Questionnaires

Q1 Complete the wording on the questionnaire below. For the bottom two rows think of some new questions to ask.

Q2 Now fill in the completed questionnaire.

My Questionnaire

Please tick the appropriate box.

	None	Sci-fi	Funny	Action	Drama	Other	(Please write in here)
What kind of films do you like?							
	None	One	....	....	....	....	(Please write in here)
How many hats have you got?							
	....	....	....	....	....	....	(Please write in here)
....							
	....	....	....	....	....	....	(Please write in here)
....							

Q3 A toy shop wants to know which of their new toys is more popular. They asked local children to put their votes on this tally chart.

Fill in the totals for all three.

	TALLY	TOTAL
Robot Elephant	卌 IIII	....
Robot Duck	卌	....
Dino Robot	卌 卌 II	....

Which toy is the most popular? ....

Which toy is the least popular? ....

Q4 In a nearby town a full-sized robot duck robbed a bank. After this all the people that voted for the toy duck changed their minds and voted for the robot elephant toy.

How many votes does the robot elephant have now? ....

Is the dino robot still the most popular toy? ....

SWAG

SEE CLASSBOOK B P.22-23

Ordering and Estimating Fractions

Q1 Mark the fractions on the number lines, and write down which is bigger.

a) $\frac{2}{3}$ and $\frac{3}{4}$ ....

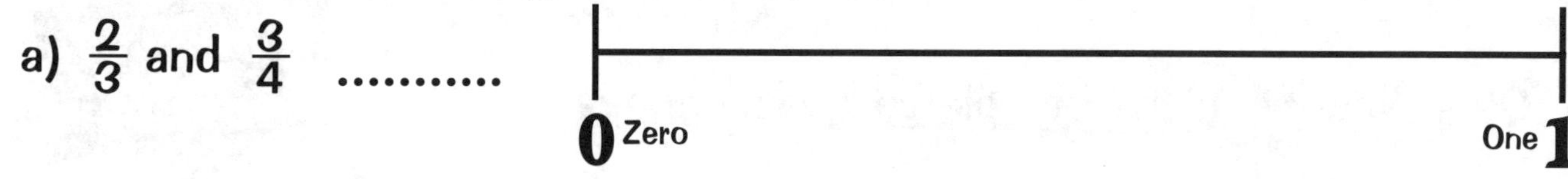

b) $\frac{1}{2}$ and $\frac{2}{5}$ ....

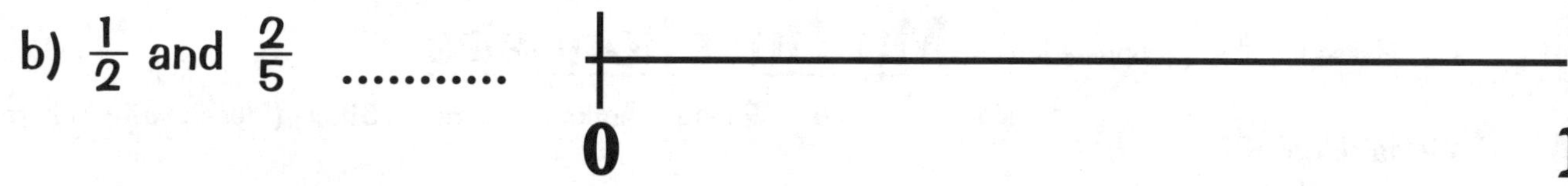

c) $\frac{1}{5}$ and $\frac{1}{3}$ ....

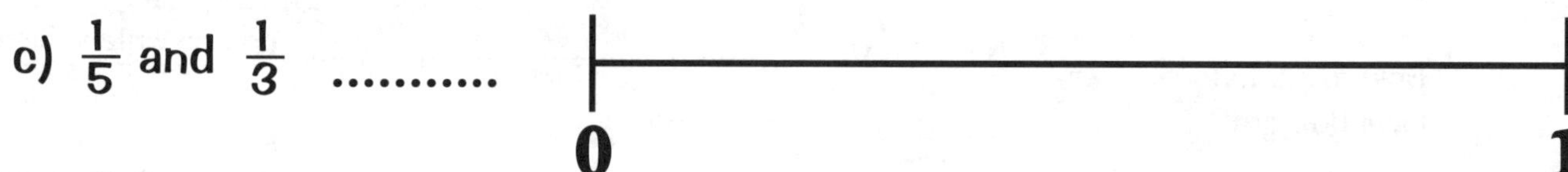

d) $\frac{1}{2}$, $\frac{3}{4}$ and $\frac{3}{5}$ ....

0 1

e) $\frac{1}{4}$, $\frac{2}{3}$ and $\frac{1}{2}$ ....

0 1

Q2 Look at these number lines and work out what the fractions are.

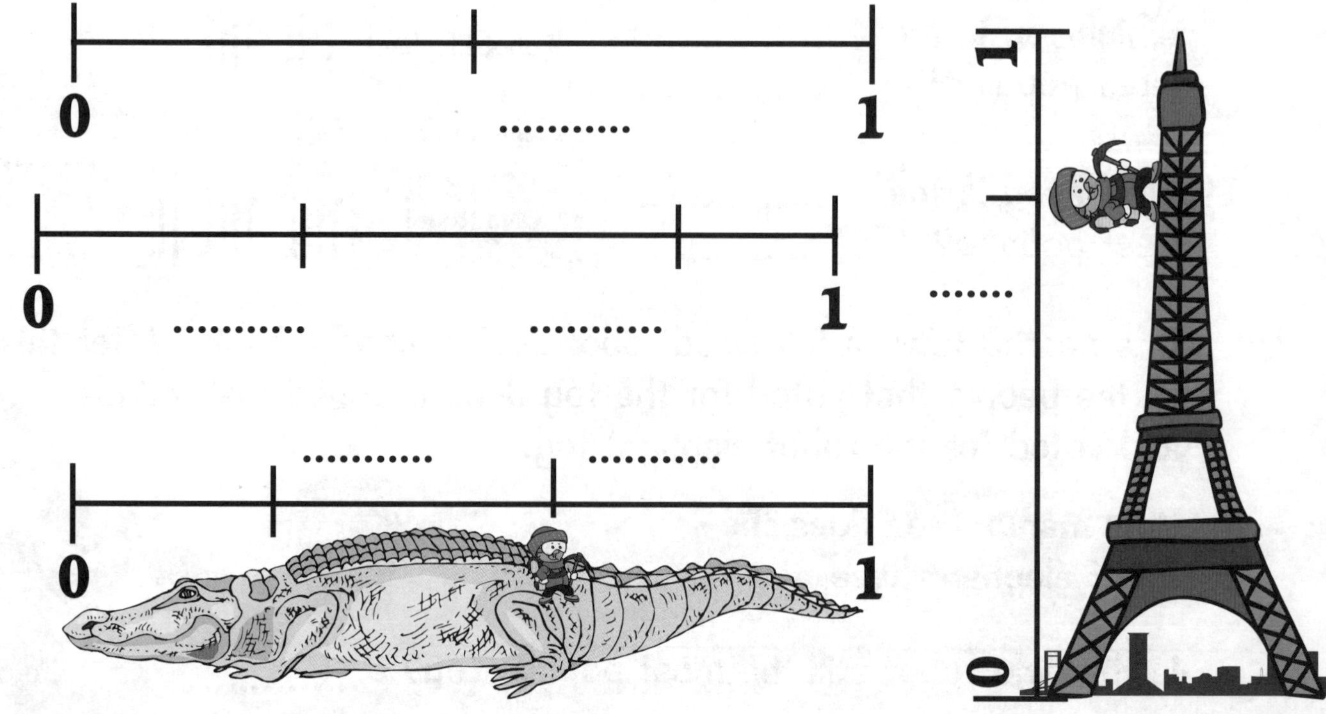

Reading Scales — Rounding

Q1 Last summer, Ugbert tried to ride his mammoth to the end of the number line. How far is he, to the nearest half, in each of the photos?

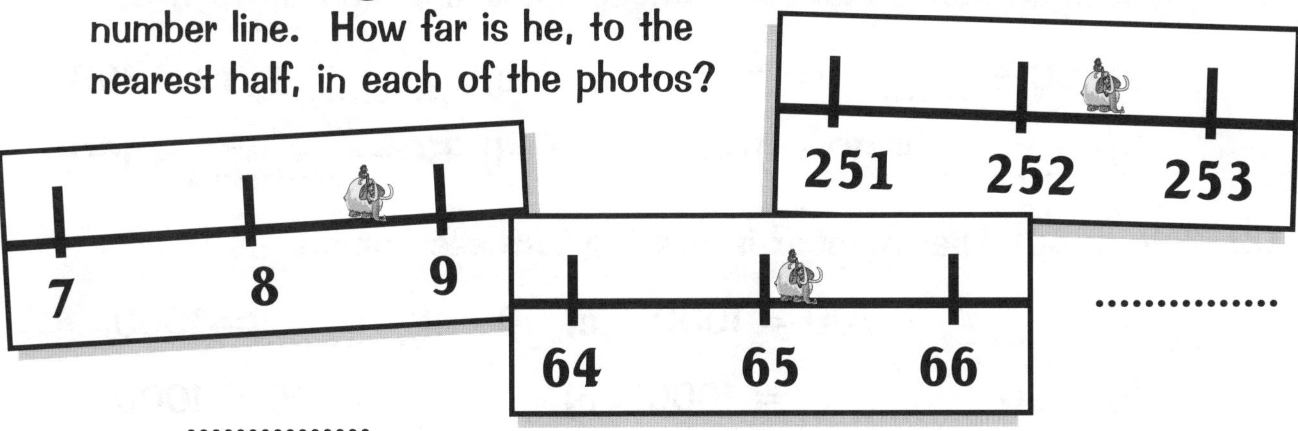

....

....

....

Q2 Write down these measurements to the nearest half m.

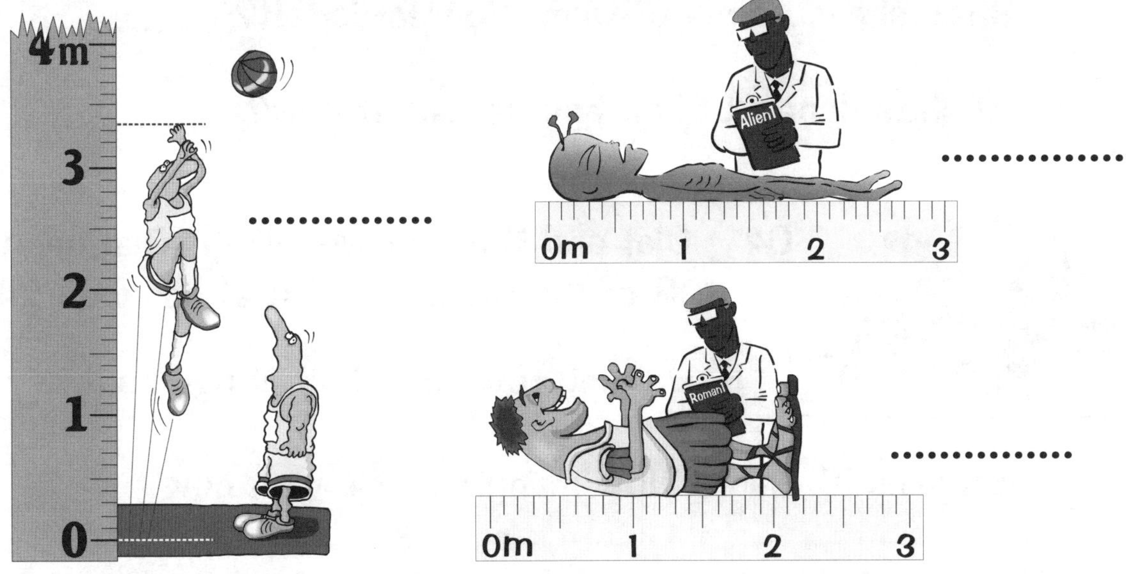

....

....

....

Q3 Write these measurements to the nearest half litre, or half kilogram.

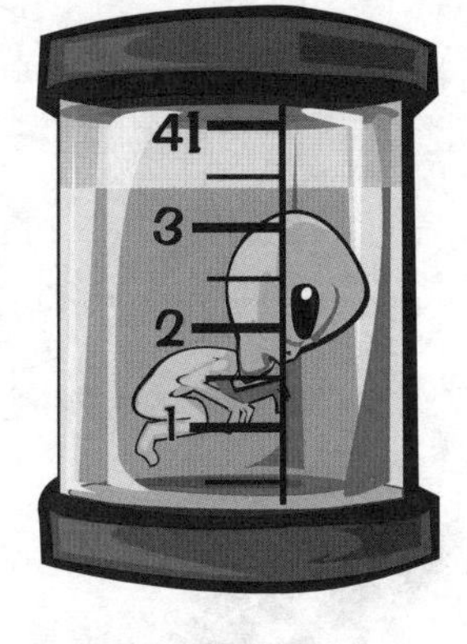

....

 SEE CLASSBOOK B P.26-27

Text Sums and Missing Numbers

Q1 Find the missing number in these sums that add up to 100.

a) 90 + ... = 100　　c) .... + 30 = 100

b) .... + 80 = 100　　d) 50 + ... = 100

Q2 Work out what number is missing in these sums.

a) .... + 700 = 1000　　c) 100 + ... = 1000

b) 600 + ... = 1000　　d) .... +200 = 1000

Q3 Jungle June is on her way to Tibet, which is 1000km away from her house.

She's already done 300km. How far is left? ....

If she's done 600km, how far is left now? ....

Q4 Olaf and Uraf are wrestling. Olaf has won 13 of the rounds, and Uraf has won 24.

How many rounds is that altogether? ....

Uraf wins 16 more. How many has she won now? ....

Q5 Now that Nobby Nimbus has made himself a pair of wings, he can fly all the way to school.

There were 150 feathers in his wings, but 60 of them fell out. How many are there now?

....

When he has just 85 feathers, he'll drop like a stone. How much less than 150 is 85?

....

Mental Strategies — Number Lines

Q1 Use the number lines to add these numbers up.

a) 29 + 25 = 29 + 20 + 5 = ...

b) 18 + 45 = ... = ...

45

c) 52 + 34 = ... = ...

52

d) 47 + 26 = ... = ...

e) 14 + 51 = ... = ...

Q2 Do these sums, using the number line.
(Remember to count up from the smaller number.)

a) 25 – 18 = 2 + 5 = ...

+...... +......
18 20 25

b) 32 – 13 = ... = ...

13

c) 56 – 27 = ... = ...

27

d) 44 – 35 = ... = ...

Q3 Jim-Bob and Binsi are cooking hotdogs by belching fire on them. Use the thermometer as a number line to work these out.

The hot dogs were 23°C. Jim-Bob heats his hotdog by just 18°C more. How hot is it now?

....

Binsi's hotdog is 37°C hotter than Jim-Bob's. How hot is that?

....

0 23 100

SEE CLASSBOOK B P.32-33

Sums in Columns

Q1 Work out these sums (write your answers in the right columns).

a)	b)	c)	d)	e)
24	47	16	33	83
+ 15	+ 22	+ 51	+ 45	+ 19
9 +	....	....	....	....
30	....	....	....	....
39	....	....	....	....

Q2 In the Piggy Back Space Race, Ted and Fred are behind with 26 orbits. Fran and Jan are 53 orbits ahead.

How many orbits have Fran and Jan done?

(Write out the sum in columns.)

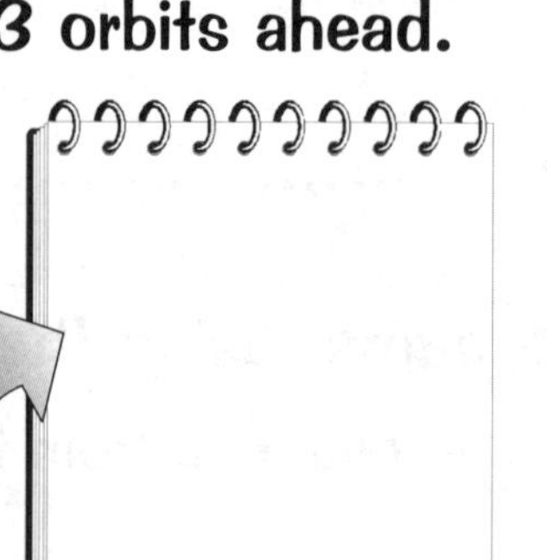

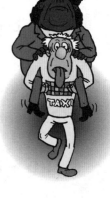

Q3 Work out the answers to these sums, using easier numbers.

a)	b)	c)	d)	e)
62	35	53	42	68
− 39	− 24	− 22	− 31	− 44
22 (subtract 40 (not 39))	....	....	....	....
+ 1 (add the 1 back on)	....	....	....	....
23	....	....	....	....

Q4 Chimbo and Wes are doing sponsored leaps. Wes has done 64 leaps. Chimbo has done 86.

How many more leaps has little Chimbo done?

(Write out the sum in columns.)

Measures — Changing Units

Q1 Two and a half metres is 2m 50cm. Finish off the following.

a) 6 and a half metres is ...... m .... cm.

b) 2 and a half kilograms is ...... kg .... g.

c) 7 and a half pounds is £ ...... and .... pence.

d) 9 and a half centimetres is ...... cm .... mm.

Q2 Say what these measurements are, in mixed units.

a) 6790g ...... kg .... g

b) 2456m ...... km .... m

c) 4350l ...... l .... ml

d) 106cm ...... m .... cm

Q3 Write the following as metres and centimetres.

a) 2560mm ....

b) 4120mm ....

Q4 Write these amounts in different units by putting in a dot.

a) 250cm ...2.5... m

b) 1 and a half metres .... m

c) 7450g .... kg

d) 350 pence £ ....

e) 49mm .... cm

f) 680cm .... m

Q5 Wrestler Tiny Tony only weighs 52 kg 50g.

Write down Tony's weight using a dot.

.... kg

How much does Tony weigh in grams?

.... grams

See Classbook B P.36-37

Shapes — Rotations & Right Angles

Q1 How many turns are these? Whole, half or quarter?

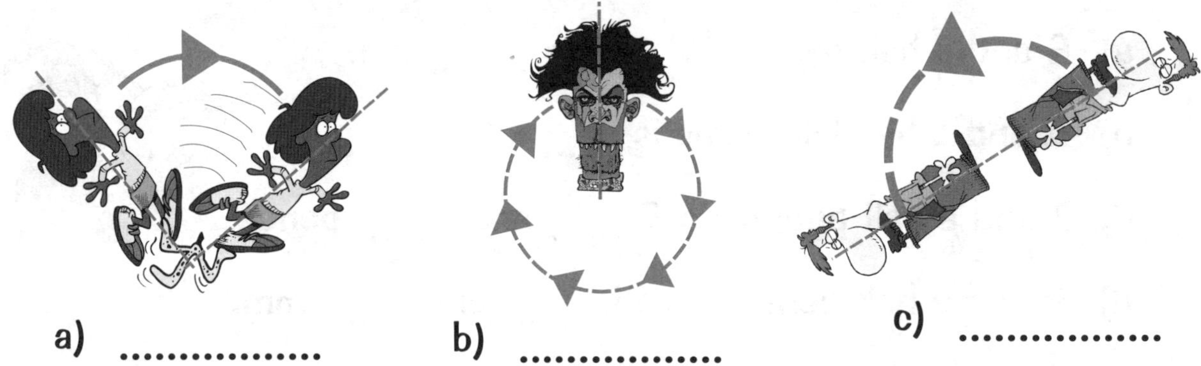

a) .... b) .... c) ....

Q2 Put a ring around all the right angles in these shapes.

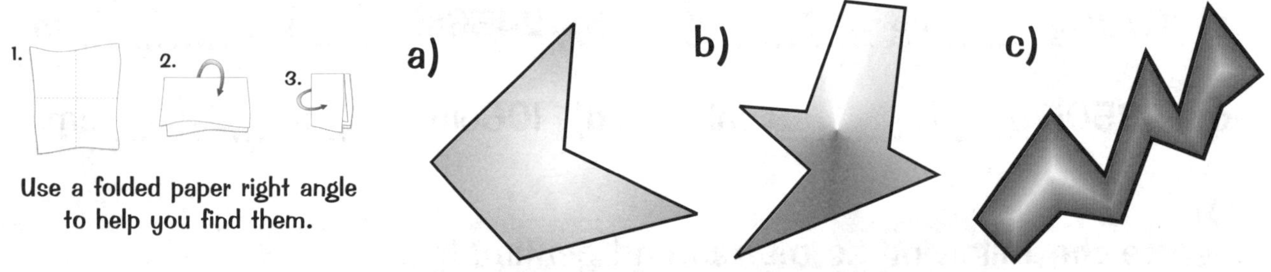

Use a folded paper right angle to help you find them.

Q3 Use your paper right angle to say whether these angles are bigger or smaller than a right angle.

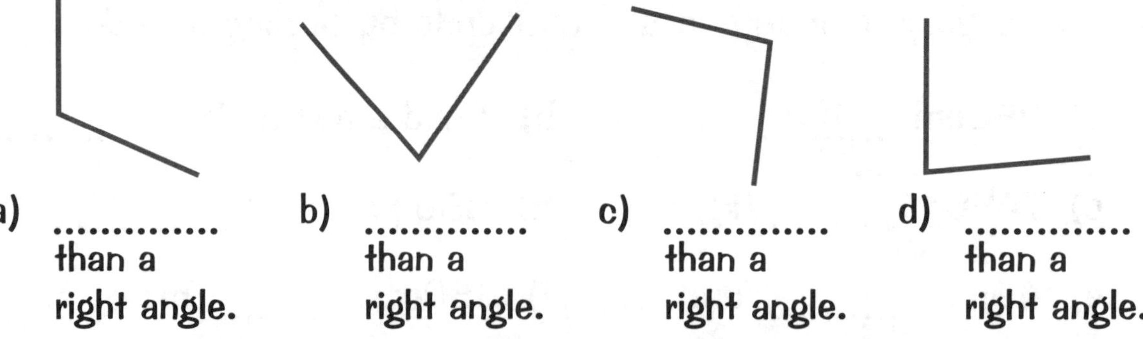

a) .... than a right angle.

b) .... than a right angle.

c) .... than a right angle.

d) .... than a right angle.

Q4 These pictures need right angles to finish them. Draw along the edges of your paper right angle to join the crosses.

Reasoning About Shapes

Q1 Draw a blue ring around all the four-sided shapes you can see.
Draw a red ring around all the shapes with sides the same length.

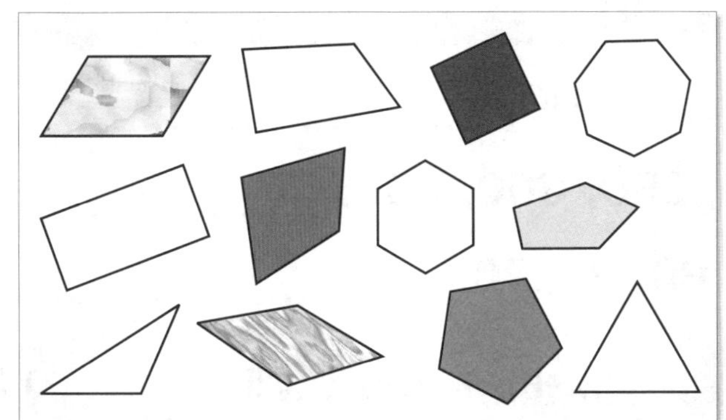

Are there any shapes that are in both rings?

Yes ☐ No ☐

Q2 Draw a ring around the shape that doesn't belong where it is.

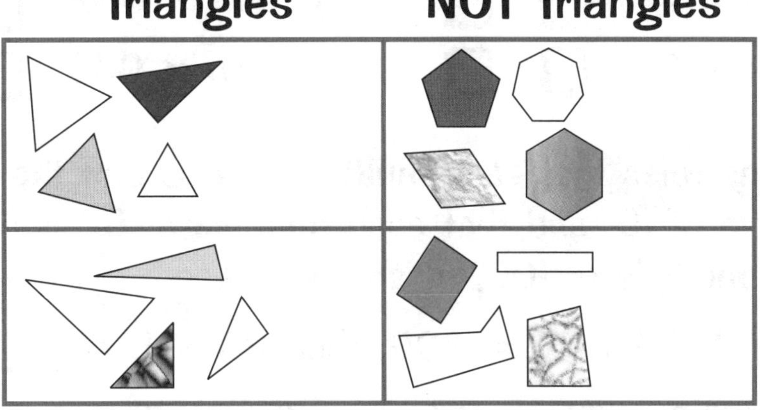

For each group, draw in another shape that fits.

Q3 Write down the right labels for these groups of shapes.

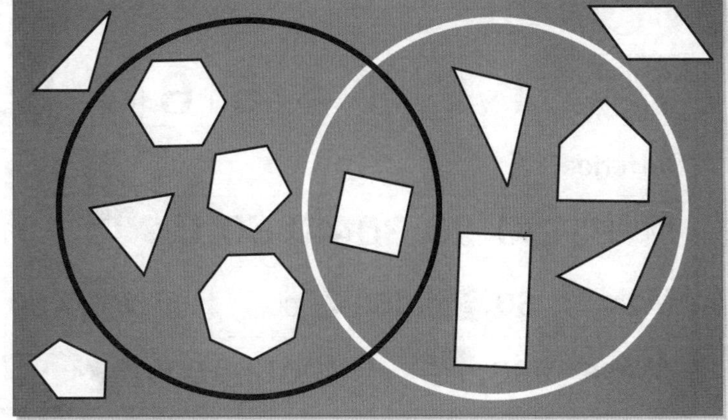

Black Ring:

....

....

White Ring:

....

....

SEE CLASSBOOK B P.42-43

Numbers & Counting — Multiple Rules

Q1 Work out whether these are multiples of 2, 5, 10 or 50, and then fill in the next 4 multiples.

a) ...12, 14, 16, 18, 20, ...

b) ...40, 50, 60, 70, 80, ...

c) ...150, 200, 250, 300, 350, ...

d) ...50, 55, 60, 65, 70, ...

Q2 Say whether the answers to these sums will be even or odd, without working them out.

	EVEN	ODD
a) 9 × 3	☐	☐
b) 6 × 4	☐	☐
c) 11 × 5	☐	☐
d) Even × Even	☐	☐
e) Odd × Odd	☐	☐
f) Even × Odd	☐	☐

Q3 Use the rules that each multiple of 5 is half the same multiple of 10, and that each multiple of 50 is half the same multiple of 100, to answer these.

a) If 36 × 10 = 360, then 36 × 5 = ...

b) If 9 × 50 = 450, then 9 × 100 = ...

c) If 22 × 100 = 2200, then 22 × 50 = ...

d) If 14 × 5 = 70, then 14 × 10 = ...

Q4 Fill in the gaps in this table of multiples, using what you know about the rules for multiples of 5, 10, 50 and 100.

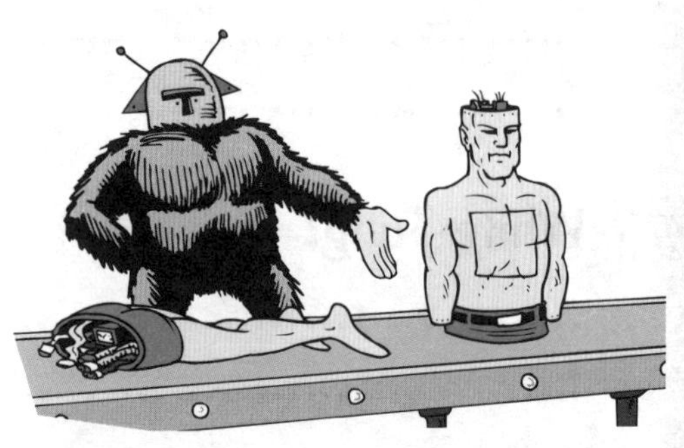

Number of Robots	1	2	3	4	5	6	7	8	9	10
Batteries	5					[illegible]	[illegible]	40	45	[illegible]
Fingers	10	20	30	40	50	[illegible]	[illegible]			
Motors	50	[illegible]	150	[illegible]			[illegible]	400	450	[illegible]
Wires	100	[illegible]		400	500	600	[illegible]			[illegible]

Understanding ×/÷ With Remainders

Q1 Work out the answers to these exact division sums.

a) $9 \div 3 =$ .... b) $15 \div 3 =$ ....

c) $20 \div 5 =$ .... d) $36 \div 3 =$ ....

e) $28 \div 7 =$ .... f) $45 \div 5 =$ ....

Q2 38 pizzas are shared between 6 greedy brothers.

How many pizzas does each brother get?

....

How many pizzas are left over?

....

Q3 Fill in the answers to these questions.

a) $32 \div 3 = 10$ remainder .... b) $23 \div 5 = 4$ remainder ....

c) $25 \div 4 = 6$ remainder .... d) $31 \div 7 =$ .... remainder ....

e) $9 \div 3 =$ .... remainder .... f) $16 \div 3 =$ .... remainder ....

Q4 Fill in the missing remainders in these multiplication sums.

a) $19 = 5 \times 3 + \square$ $3 \times 5 = 15$ $19 - 15 = 4$ ....

b) $30 = 4 \times 7 + \square$ ....

c) $44 = 8 \times 5 + \square$ ....

d) $21 = 3 \times 6 + \square$ ....

e) $29 = 5 \times 5 + \square$

....

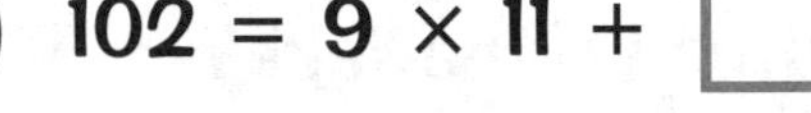

f) $102 = 9 \times 11 + \square$

....

Did someone say reindeer?

SEE CLASSBOOK B P.48-51

Remainders and Rounding

Q1 A school has 32 hockey sticks to be shared between 3 teams.

If each team gets an equal number of sticks, how many will each team get?

....

How many sticks are left over?

....

Q2 Every day 6 new recruits join the fish army.

The fish army has 40 fish soldiers in total after 6 days. How many fish were in the army to start off with?

....

I love rounding things up!

Q3 Round up the answers to these sums:

a) 9 ÷ 2 = ... b) 22 ÷ 5 = ...

c) 16 ÷ 7 = ... d) 35 ÷ 10 = ...

Q4 Now round these ones down:

a) 10 ÷ 3 = ... b) 23 ÷ 4 = ...

c) 72 ÷ 7 = ... d) 47 ÷ 8 = ...

Q5 You have to decide whether you need to round these up or round them down, and then work them out.

With each chop, Louise can break 5 blocks. She wants to break 53 blocks. How many chops must she do?

....

Her friend takes a photo every time she breaks 4 or more blocks at once. How many photos will he take?

....

Adding Fractions

Q1 Shade the shapes below:

I know all about halves...

a) $\frac{1}{2}$

b) $\frac{2}{4}$

Q2 Are these fractions the same as each other or not?

a) $\frac{5}{8}$ and $\frac{1}{2}$ Yes No

b) $\frac{3}{4}$ and $\frac{2}{3}$ Yes No

c) $\frac{1}{4}$ and $\frac{2}{8}$ Yes No

d) $\frac{2}{6}$ and $\frac{1}{3}$ Yes No

e) $\frac{1}{4}$ and $\frac{4}{8}$ Yes No

f) $\frac{5}{8}$ and $\frac{2}{3}$ Yes No

Q3 Halve numbers twice to answer this question...

If Douglas has eight dog biscuits, and eats half on one day, and half of the dog biscuits that are left the next day...

Dog biscuits? They told me they were chocolate chip!

a) How many biscuits does Douglas have left at the end of the second day?

....

b) What fraction of the original number of biscuits does Douglas have left?

....

Q4 These both add up to one, fill in the spaces with the correct fraction...

a)

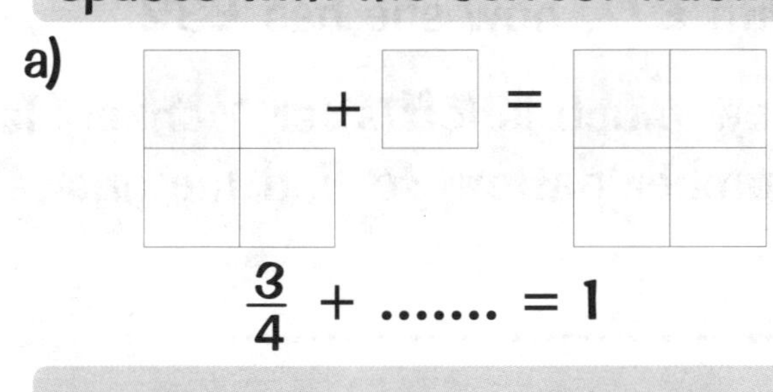

$\frac{3}{4}$ + ... = 1

b)

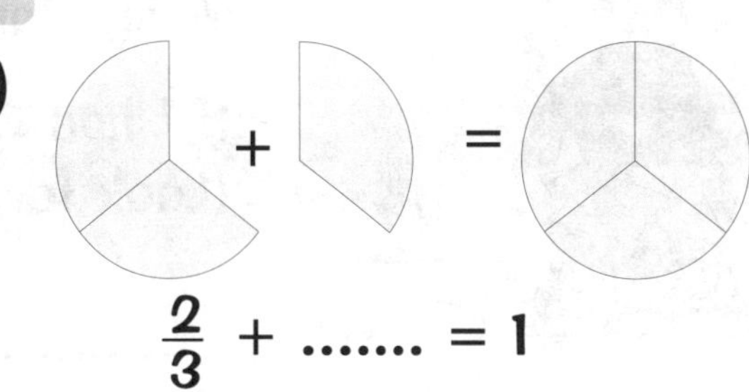

$\frac{2}{3}$ + ... = 1

Q5 Do these fractions add up to one?

a) $\frac{1}{2} + \frac{1}{2}$ Yes No

b) $\frac{1}{3} + \frac{1}{2}$ Yes No

c) $\frac{2}{3} + \frac{1}{3}$ Yes No

d) $\frac{3}{4} + \frac{1}{4}$ Yes No

SEE CLASSBOOK B P.56-59

Number Patterns

Q1 After the first couple of sums you should see a number pattern to help you finish them off without working them out.

6 + 28 = 34

a) 16 + 28 = ...

b) 26 + 28 = ...

c) 36 + 28 = ...

d) 46 + 28 = ...

e) 56 + 28 = ...

39 + 15 = 54

f) 49 + 15 = ...

g) 59 + 15 = ...

h) 69 + 15 = ...

i) 79 + 15 = ...

j) 89 + 15 = ...

Q2 Work out the first of these sums, then fill all the missing numbers in.

a) 24 – 17 = ...

b) 34 – 17 = ...

c) 44 – 17 = ...

d) 54 – 17 = ...

e) 64 – 17 = ...

f) 63 – 36 = ...

g) 73 – 36 = ...

h) 83 – 36 = ...

i) 93 – 36 = ...

j) 103 – 36 = ...

Q3 Everyone pays £45 Monkey Tax. Bongo started with £67, and is left with £22 after he's paid. Molly started with £77, now she has £32.

If I had £87, how much is left after Monkey Tax? (Look for the number pattern to find the answer.)

....

Q4 If Monkey Tax were £33 instead, how much would we each have left? (After the first one the others are easy.)

a) Bongo ....

b) Molly ....

c) Me ....

See Classbook B P.60-61

Mental Strategies With Number Lines

Q1 Using the number lines, add these numbers up.

a) 250 + 150 = 250 + 100 + 50 = 400

b) 340 + 120 = ...

c) 130 + 260 = ...

d) 110 + 175 = ...

e) 494 + 146 = ...

Q2 Use the number lines to help you subtract these numbers.

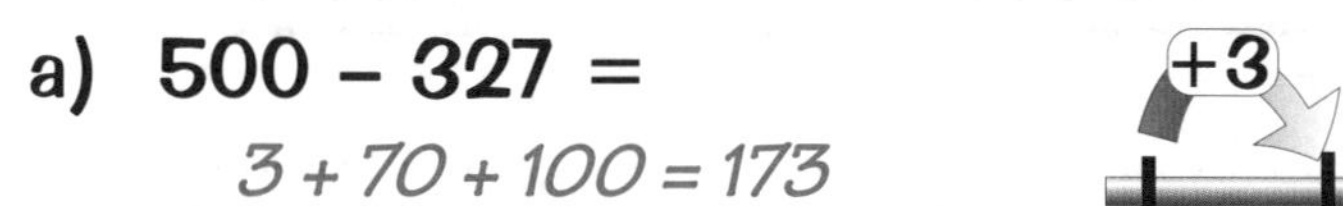

a) 500 − 327 =

3 + 70 + 100 = 173

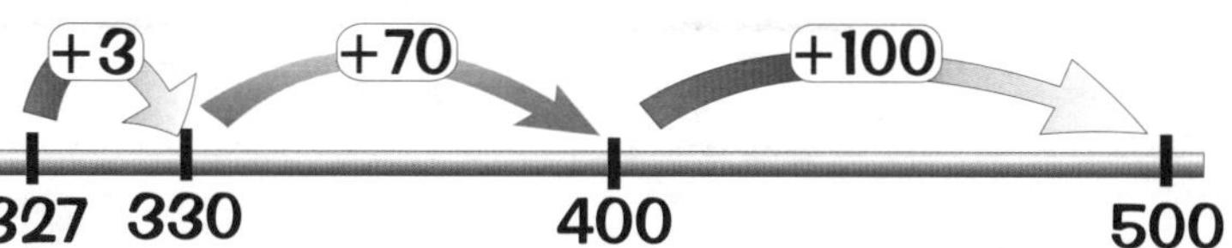

b) 500 − 269 =

....

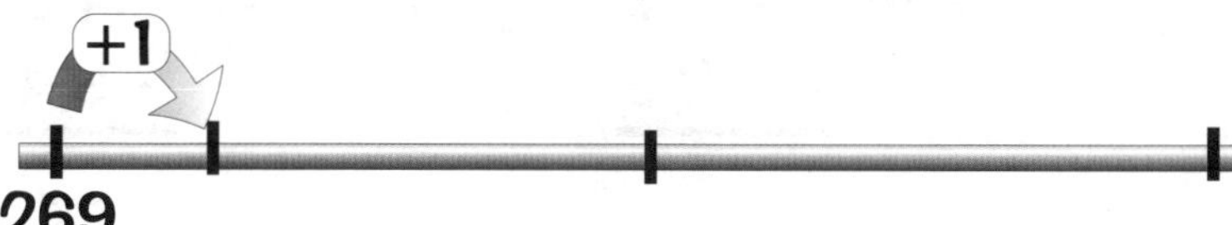

c) 650 − 343 =

....

d) 755 − 186 =

....

Q3 Sam had 635 plums, but then Barny stuffed 168 of them into his cheeks.

Sketch a number line and use it to find how many plums Sam has now.

....

SEE CLASSBOOK B P.62-63

Sums in Columns

Q1 Work out the answers to these addition sums.

a) 864 + 132 = ...

b) 237 + 511 = ...

c) 592 + 306 = ...

d) 463 + 525 = ...

e) 601 + 187 = ...

f) 358 + 240 = ...

Q2 Now you get to work out these subtraction sums, what fun... Watch out for any that need 'borrowing'.

a) 162 − 51 = ...

b) 348 − 136 = ...

c) 516 − 204 = ...

d) 872 − 436 = ...

e) 455 − 341 = ...

f) 973 − 825 = ...

Q3 More of the same, but you have to write them out in columns first.

a) 469 + 530

b) 215 + 783

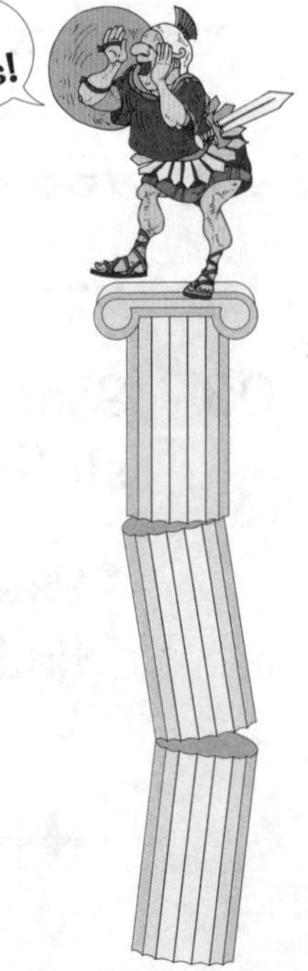

c) 654 – 142

d) 321 – 107

SEE CLASSBOOK B P.64-66

Time Additions

Q1 How many...

a) seconds in 3 minutes? .... b) minutes in 6 hours? ....

c) hours in 4 days? .... d) months in 5 years? ....

Q2 There are two ways of writing down a date.
Put the other way of writing each of these.

a) 12/07/1977 ....

b) 4th February 2001 ....

c) 31/12/1999 ....

Q3 Work out these additions of time.

a) 11:06 + 54 minutes =

....

b) 8:37 + half an hour =

....

c) Half past 2 + 40 minutes =

....

d) 1:55 + 20 minutes =

....

Q4 Answer these time sums.

a) 8 seconds + 55 seconds
= ....

b) 35 minutes + half an hour
= ....

c) 2 hours + 120 minutes
= ....

d) 40 seconds + 25 seconds
= ....

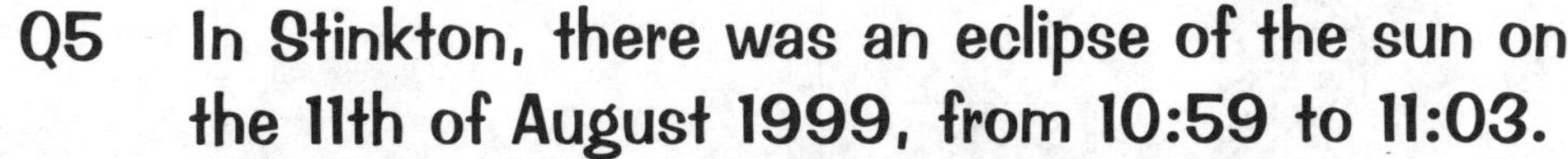

Q5 In Stinkton, there was an eclipse of the sun on the 11th of August 1999, from 10:59 to 11:03.

Write out this date in another way.

....

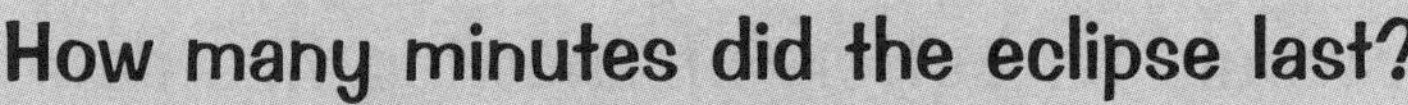

How many minutes did the eclipse last?

....

If it had lasted 180 more seconds, at what time would it have ended? ....

SEE CLASSBOOK B P.67-69

Handling Data — Tallies & Pictograms

Q1 Mervin has been eating his school books again.

Fill in the tally marks and totals in the table below.

Number of books eaten by Mervin

1 drawing = 2 books

Number of books

Breakfast Elevenses Lunch Supper Midnight Feast

Meal Time	Tally	Number of Books
Breakfast		
Elevenses		
Lunch		
Supper		
Midnight Feast		

Q2 Olivia's job is to smash computers to bits.

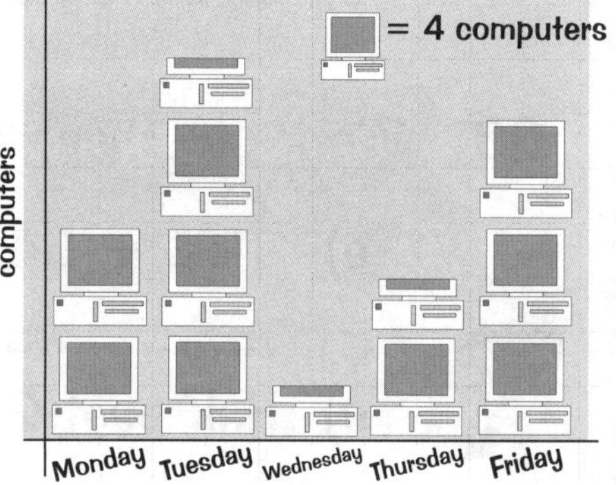

How many were smashed

a) on Tuesday? ....

b) on Thursday? ....

How many more were smashed on Monday than on Wednesday?

c) ....

Q3 **Use the table below to draw a pictogram on the graph paper. Use a scale of one drawing to one plate.**

Person	Plates Thrown
Tony	3
Martha	1
Digby	4
Daley	2
Helen	5

Q4 **Which type of graph would be better for showing this data — a pictogram or a bar chart?**

Hair Colour	Blonde	Ginger	Black	Green	Purple
Frequency	34	36	31	37	40

....

SEE CLASSBOOK B P.70-73